BIOLOGY HOMEWORK

for OCR A

FOR DOUBLE AND SEPARATE AWARDS

Jackie Clegg and Elaine Gill

Series editor: Bob McDuell

Heinemann Educational Publishers,
Halley Court, Jordan Hill, Oxford, OX2 8EJ
A division of Reed Educational & Professional Publishing Ltd
Heinemann is a registered trademark of Reed Educational & Professional Publishing Limited

OXFORD MELBOURNE AUCKLAND
JOHANNESBURG BLANTYRE GABORONE
IBADAN PORTSMOUTH NH (USA) CHICAGO

First published 2001

ISBN 0 435 58291 7

05 04 03 02 01
10 9 8 7 6 5 4 3 2 1

Edited by Helen Barham PhD

Typeset and illustrated by 🐦 Tek-Art, Croydon, Surrey

Printed and bound in Great Britain by Scotprint, East Lothian

Acknowledgements

The authors and publishers would like to thank the following for permission to use extracts/graphs/artwork:

4.1 Q1 a–c *Workbook for Science 'D level' Chemistry and Biology* Mike Taylor/Elaine Gill, Federal Publications Singapore. 4.2 Q2 *Comprehensive Biology – A course for O level* 3rd edition. Lam Peng Kwan, Federal Publications Singapore. 4.2 Q3 *Workbook for Science 'D level' Chemistry and Biology* Mike Taylor/Elaine Gill, Federal Publications Singapore. 4.3 Q1 Q2 *Comprehensive Biology – A course for O level* 3rd edition. Lam Peng Kwan, Federal Publications Singapore. 4.3 Q2 *NCS Biology* Longman. 4.3 Q3 (graph) *Human Physical Health* Cambridge Educational. 5.2 Q1 (adapted) OCR 1794/02 June 2000. 5.2 Q2 *Workbook for Science 'D level' Chemistry and Biology* Mike Taylor/Elaine Gill, Federal Publications Singapore. 5.3 Q4 Q2 *NCS Biology* Longman. 6.2 Q1 Q2 *Comprehensive Biology – A course for O level* 3rd edition. Lam Peng Kwan, Federal Publications Singapore. 6.4 Q1 (adapted) *Workbook for Science 'D level' Chemistry and Biology* Mike Taylor/Elaine Gill, Federal Publications Singapore. 6.4 Q4 *Revise GCSE Biology* Hodder and Stoughton. 9.3(1) (adapted) *Workbook for Science 'D level' Chemistry and Biology* Mike Taylor/Elaine Gill, Federal Publications Singapore. 7.8 Q6 *GCSE Questions and Answers for Biology* Jackie Callaghan and Morton Jenkins, Letts. 8.2 Q5/8.5 Q3 *Biology for You* Gareth Williams, Stanley Thornes. 9.3(1) Q3 OCR 1794/02 June 2001. 10.1 Q4 OCR 1974 Biology Higher 1999. 10.2 Q3 *Biology for You* Gareth Williams, Stanley Thornes. 10.3 Q4 MEG syllabus C and D, Test 4 1994. 10.4 Q2 MEG syllabus C and D, Test 4 1995. 10.6 Q4 *GCSE Questions and Answers for Biology* Jackie Callaghan and Morton Jenkins 1999, Letts. A1.1 Q1 (table) Heinz. A1.4 Q5 Toole and Toole *Understanding Biology for A level* 4th Edition, Nelson Thornes. A1.5 Q2 (adapted diagram) Q2 *Comprehensive Biology – A course for O level* 3rd edition. Lam Peng Kwan, Federal Publications Singapore. A2.3 Q1/Q5 (adapted) OCR 1794/02 June 1999. A2.3 Q4 (adapted) *Revise GCSE Biology* Hodder and Stoughton. A3.2 Q1 OCR 1780/03 June 1999. A4.2 Q4 (adapted) OCR 1780/03 June 1999. A4.3 Q1 OCR 1785/04 June 1997. A4.4 Q1 (adapted) OCR 1785/04 June 1998. A4.5 Q4 (adapted) 1785/04 June 1998.

The publishers have made every effort to trace the copyright holders, but if they have inadvertently overlooked any, they will be pleased to make the necessary arrangements at the first opportunity.

5.1 Science Photo Library

Introduction

This book provides homework for students taking Biology as part of OCR A double-award science or OCR A separate-award biology. It accompanies the student course books for OCR A double-award and separate-award biology (ISBNs 0 435 58297 6 and 0 435 58296 8, respectively).

There is one page of homework for each double-page spread in the student course book. This makes it easy to see which homework may be set following lessons based on a particular double-page spread.

Where students can take the course book home, this homework book will supply extra work to be done at home. Where the course book is not available, the homework book provides:

- a list of key points for each spread
- important diagrams such as the carbon cycle and nitrogen cycle for reference
- the full and detailed glossary from the separate-award biology course book.

The answers to the questions in the homework book are available on the CD-ROM. They can be used to mark the work or can be printed out and given to students to mark their own work.

The questions in the homework book can be used in lessons where the teacher is absent. Students can work through the relevant double-page spread in the student course book and then attempt questions from the homework book. They could then be given the answers from the CD-ROM towards the end of the lesson.

The homework book allows differentiated homework to be set if required. The questions in the homework book are set at three levels:

- ■ standard demand – aimed at C and D grades
- ◆ standard/high demand – aimed at A and B grades
- ◇ high demand – aimed at A* grade.

IDEAS AND EVIDENCE questions focus on how science is evaluated and presented, and the power and limitations of science in addressing industrial, social and environmental issues.

Material marked with an **H** is for higher-tier only.

For students needing further help there is additional material on the CD-ROM that accompanies the Teacher Resource Pack which can be modified to suit the individual needs of students. This could be put together as a booklet for each Teaching block, perhaps incorporating Key-stage 3 Summary sheets and modified Student checklists where statements in bold (H only) are removed.

We hope that this Homework book will help students to be successful.

Contents

1.1 Cells

Key points

- All cells have certain structures in common, no matter what type of organism they come from.

- There are some differences between animal cells and plant cells

1 Tim used a light microscope to look at some onion cells. The diagram below shows what he saw.

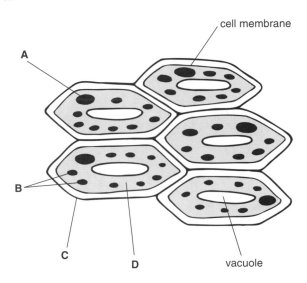

a Copy the diagram and complete labels A–D.

b List those structures that are only found in plant cells.

c Copy and complete the following table.

cell structure	function
nucleus	
	controls the movement of substances into and out of the cell
chloroplasts	
	contains cell sap for storage and support
cytoplasm	

d Tim expected to see other structures in the onion cells. Explain why Tim did not see chloroplasts and mitochondria.

2 Year-7 students often confuse cells with atoms. Write an information sheet for Year-7 students to explain the difference between cells and atoms.

3 Some books describe the nucleus as the 'brain of the cell'. Give reasons for and against the use of this statement.

4 All the activities of the cell are aided by protein substances produced by the cytoplasm. These protein substances are called enzymes. There are many thousands of enzymes in the body. They are referred to as biological catalysts. Every cell contains enzymes that speed up respiration. Some types of cells in our bodies contain enzymes that are not found in any other types of cells.

a Explain why enzymes are referred to as biological catalysts.

b Explain why every cell contains enzymes that speed up respiration.

c Suggest a reason why certain types of cell contain enzymes that are not found in any other types of cell.

IDEAS AND EVIDENCE

5 Robert Hooke was the first person to observe cells through a microscope. In 1676, Anton van Leeuwenhoek noticed that all living material was made up of cells. By 1839, the quality of microscopes had improved and details of cells could be observed. Schwann and Schleiden proposed The Cell Theory.

Draw a time line to show the developments in science that have helped our understanding of the cell.

1.2 Life processes

Key points

- Organisms need to carry out certain life processes in order to stay alive.

- Cells working together as tissues, organs and systems carry out these processes.

1

a Suggest why the alien thinks that the car is a living thing.

b Write a detailed description for the alien, explaining why the car is not a living thing.

2 Copy and complete the following table.

organs	system
trachea and lungs	
	digestive
ovaries, oviducts and uterus	
	nervous
kidneys and bladder	

3 Draw labelled diagrams to show the levels of organisation in the circulatory system.

4 List which of the seven life processes are involved in each of the following activities:

a eating your lunch;

b going to the toilet;

c a plant growing towards the sun;

d a frog producing tadpoles;

e running to catch the bus.

5 Plants are capable of movement; animals are capable of movement and locomotion.

Explain the difference between movement and locomotion, giving examples of each.

6 The diagrams below show some specialised cells.

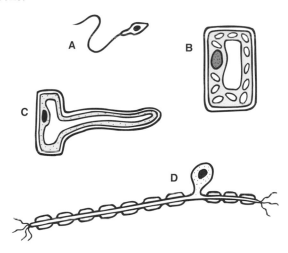

a Name each of the cell types A–D.

b Explain how the structure of each cell A–D helps it to carry out its function.

7 The following words refer to movement in plants.

- geotropism
- phototropism

Find out the meaning of these words. Write a sentence for each word, describing the type of plant movement involved.

1.3 Transport and cells

1 Copy the paragraph below, using words from the following list to fill in the gaps.

You may use each word once, more than once or not at all.

- active • concentration • diffusion • enter
- gradient • high • leave • low • membrane
- osmosis • respiration • transport

The cell _____ controls which substances enter or _____ the cell. The movement of substances from an area where they are in a low _____ to an area of _____ concentration is called _____ _____. Moving substances against a _____ _____ requires energy. This energy comes from _____.

2 Take a glass of cold water and put a teaspoonful of jam in the bottom of the glass. Leave it for two days and observe the results. Draw the results and explain what has happened.

3 A person wearing perfume enters a room. After a few minutes, people at the back of the room can smell the perfume. Using diagrams to help, explain the movement of perfume molecules across the room.

4 Copy and complete the following table.

name of movement	description of movement
diffusion	
	the diffusion of water molecules from a high water concentration to a lower water concentration through a partially permeable membrane
active transport	

5 Oxygen diffuses across the alveoli from the lungs into the blood. Carbon dioxide diffuses in the opposite direction. Explain what makes this happen.

6 The diagram below shows the movement of water across a root.

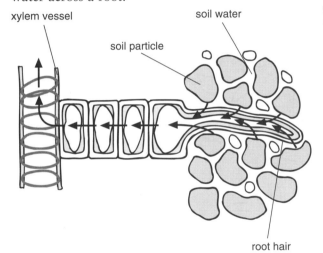

a Describe your journey as a water molecule from the soil to the leaf of a plant.

b Explain why water is able to enter the root.

c Explain how mineral salts enter the root.

d Gardeners raise seedlings in trays of compost. When the seedlings are large enough, the gardener removes them from the trays and replants them in the garden. For the first few days the seedlings wilt, even though the gardener waters them regularly. Explain why the seedlings wilt.

7 Design and construct an animated poster or model to explain active transport across the cell membrane. You should include at least three stages, showing how:

- substances outside the cell combine with the carrier molecule;

- the carrier molecule transports substances across the membrane using energy from ATP;

- substances are released inside the cell.

1.4 Osmosis

Key points

- Water can go in or out of cells by osmosis, which is a special type of diffusion.
- **H** Osmosis can occur because cell membranes are partially permeable.

- Osmosis is a very important process that enables plants to support themselves.

---

1 Copy the following grid. Answer the questions and fill in the grid to discover the key word.

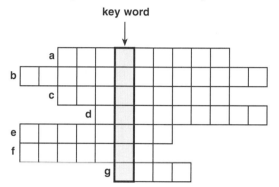

key word

a The place in the cell where chemical reactions occur.

b In an experiment, potato chips were placed in various concentrations of _____ _____ .

c Osmosis can occur because cell membranes are partially _____ .

d Water will move from a solution that has a high water _____ .

e Plastic tubing that acts like a cell membrane.

f If placed in concentrated sugar solution, a cell loses water by osmosis and the cell becomes _____ .

g In an experiment, potato chips were placed in distilled water. They took in water and increased in _____ .

2 Describe the difference between flaccid and turgid.

3 A bag of dialysis tubing is filled with sugar solution, then put into a beaker of distilled water. Draw a fully labelled and detailed diagram to explain why the bag becomes larger.

4 Justine does an experiment using red blood cells. She has three test tubes:

- Tube A contains distilled water.

- Tube B contains 0.85% sodium chloride solution. (This is the same concentration as the blood plasma in which red blood cells are normally bathed.)
- Tube C contains 10% sodium chloride solution.

Justine adds a few drops of blood to each tube and gently shakes the tube to disperse the red blood cells. After 20 minutes, she puts a drop of liquid from each tube onto a series of microscope slides. She observes the appearance of the red blood cells on each slide using a microscope.

a Describe the appearance of the red blood cells taken from each of the tubes A–C.

b Give reasons for the appearance of the red blood cells in each tube.

5 Mrs Fry, the school cook, soaks lettuce in salt water to remove any slugs or greenfly.

a Mrs Fry wants to know why the lettuce leaves become limp. Write an explanation for her.

b Suggest how Mrs Fry could make the lettuce leaves crisp again.

6 The table below shows the results of an investigation in which pieces of potato were placed into different concentrations of sugar solution.

% concentration of sugar solution	% change in mass of potato
5	+9
10	+4
15	+1
20	−7
25	−10

a Which concentration of sugar is closest to the concentration of potato cell sap? Give a reason for your answer.

b Write down the name of the process that causes the change in mass.

c Estimate the % concentration of sugar solution that would produce a 4% decrease in mass.

2.1 Enzymes

Key points

- The digestive system produces enzymes that break down the components of our food.
- This digestion can be demonstrated using various food tests.

1 The table below shows information about food tests.

food molecule	test	colour change
starch		brown to _____
	Benedict's solution	_____ to orange/red
protein		blue to _____

a Copy and complete the table.

b Describe how you would test a sample to show that it contained simple sugars.

2 Mark was investigating the action of pepsin. He took four pieces of capillary tubing containing uncooked egg white. He placed the tubes in a beaker of water and boiled it for 5 minutes. He then set up the apparatus as shown in the diagram below.

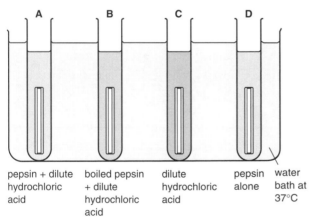

	A	B	C	D

pepsin + dilute hydrochloric acid | boiled pepsin + dilute hydrochloric acid | dilute hydrochloric acid | pepsin alone | water bath at 37°C

Mark measured the length of the egg white in each capillary tube at the start of the investigation and again after 1 hour. His results are shown in the table below.

tube	length in mm	
	start	finish
A	42	15
B	40	32
C	41	33
D	40	40

a Write a conclusion for Mark's investigation.

b Explain the changes in tubes B and C.

c Explain why Mark included tube C.

d Why did Mark keep his apparatus at 37°C?

e Mark's teacher said that he should set up one other control tube. Suggest what this should include.

f Write down the type of food molecule that pepsin acts on.

3 The graph below shows how the rate of reaction of the enzyme amylase varies with temperature.

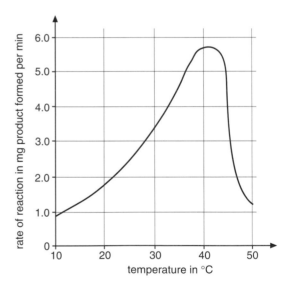

a Describe an investigation you could do to obtain a similar set of results.

b i Suggest which type of food molecule the enzyme amylase is acting on.

  ii Write down the optimum temperature for amylase.

  iii Explain what is meant by the optimum temperature.

  iv Write down the range of temperature at which amylase is fairly active.

c Explain the low rate of enzyme activity at 50°C.

4 Enzymes are used for many domestic purposes. List some of the enzymes used in your home and explain what they do.

2.2 Digestion

Key points

- The enzymes produced by the organs of the digestive system break down food molecules.
- This process of digestion is assisted by the production of chemicals from other organs.

1 The diagram below shows the digestive system and some associated organs.

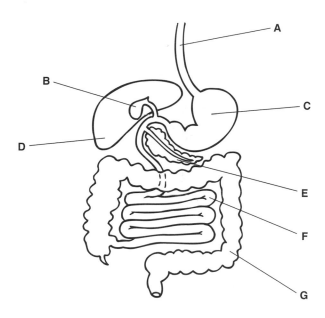

a Copy the diagram into your book and complete labels A–G.

b On your diagram:
  i colour red where conditions are acidic;
  ii colour blue where conditions are alkaline;
  iii colour yellow where bile is produced.

2 Write a letter for a young child explaining why it is important that they chew their food properly before swallowing.

3 Copy the list of parts of the body below and next to each write the correct function from the second list.

parts of body	functions
mouth	stores bile
oesophagus	produces bile
stomach	food is chewed here
liver	joins mouth to stomach
gall bladder	releases gastric juices

4 Imagine you are a cheeseburger. Write the story of your journey from the mouth to the small intestine. Make your story imaginative and factual. Include the breakdown of the different types of food molecules in the cheeseburger.

5 Explain why the digestion of fat does not really start until it reaches the small intestine.

6 Imagine you are a dietician working at your local hospital. Write a one-day menu for a patient who has gallstones. You must ensure that the patient receives a balanced but fat-free diet.

7

a Copy the lists below, matching each food molecule with the enzyme that breaks it down, and the products that are formed.

food molecules	enzymes	products
starch	protease	maltose
protein	lipase	amino acids
fats	amylase	fatty acids and glycerol

b Write down where in the digestive system each of the three enzymes listed in a starts to work on the food molecules.

8 Draw a table to show all the substances that are added to food as it passes through the digestive system. Your table should show where these substances are added and their role in digestion.

IDEAS AND EVIDENCE

9 William Beaumont experimented with gastric juices collected from the stomach wall of Alexis St Martin. Draw a poster to help Beaumont explain his findings to St Martin. Include the different types of substances discovered and their functions.

2.3 Absorption (1)

Key points

- After digestion, food molecules are absorbed from the small intestine into the bloodstream.

- The small intestine has many features that allow rapid absorption to take place.

1 Ian did an experiment using a model gut. He set up the apparatus as shown in the diagram below.

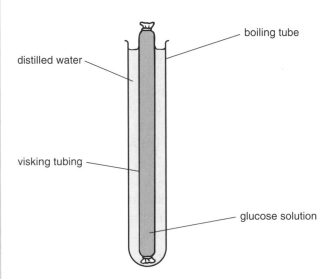

Ian tested the distilled water for the presence of glucose at the start of the experiment, then again after 15 minutes.

a Describe how Ian tested for the presence of glucose.

b After 15 minutes, Ian discovered that glucose was present in the distilled water. Draw a results table for Ian's experiment.

c Write down the name of the process that allowed glucose to move into the distilled water.

d Write down the name of the part of the digestive system represented by:
  i the visking tubing;
  ii the glucose solution;
  iii the distilled water.

e Write a conclusion for Ian's experiment.

f Describe what happens to the parts of food that are not absorbed into the blood.

2 Explain how the structure of the small intestine helps it to carry out its function. Illustrate your answer with a fully labelled diagram.

3 The diagram below shows the structure of a single villus.

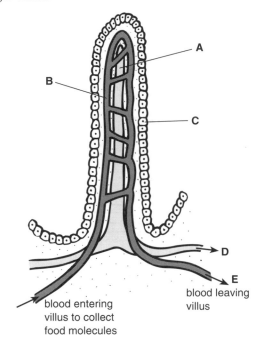

a Copy the diagram and label parts A, B and C.

b The substances in D and E are moving towards different parts of the body. Write down the names of these parts of the body.

c Which of the following food molecules will be present in the blood at E?

- amino acids • fatty acids • fibre
- glucose • glycerol • lactose • maltose
- protein • starch • sucrose

d The products of digestion of starch, protein and fats are absorbed by the small intestine. Write down the names of these products of digestion.

e Name the processes by which the products of digestion are absorbed into the blood and lymph.

4 Make a model of part of the small intestine. The model should have a smooth outside and should show the relatively increased surface area of the inside.

Continued ▶

2.3 Absorption (2)

5 Students in Year 8 learn about the digestive system and enzymes. Design a board game for Year-8 students that will reinforce their knowledge about the digestive system. Make sure you include the names of the different parts of the digestive system and their functions. Some simple characteristics of enzymes should also be included.

6 The flow chart below shows what happens to amino acid molecules as they pass into the blood to be processed by the liver.

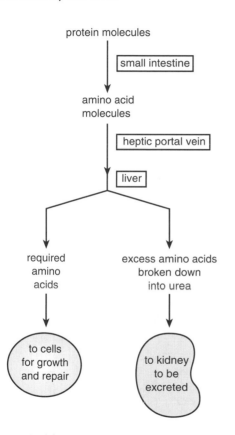

Draw a similar flow chart to show what happens to glucose molecules.

7 Write an information leaflet for a teenager who is lactose intolerant. Explain what is meant by lactose intolerant and describe the symptoms. Suggest suitable menus for two days.

8 The cheeseburger in Question 4 on page 2.2 has now been digested. Describe the fate of the fatty acids and the glycerol molecules. Include details of their journey through the lacteals, the blood stream, the liver and then into cells under the skin for storage.

9 The liver and the pancreas are organs associated with the digestive system. List the functions of these two organs that relate to the digestive system.

10 Describe what happens to a protein molecule in food, from the time it enters the mouth to the time its products are built up into a new structure in the cytoplasm of a muscle cell.

11 Write down the chemical changes that a starch molecule undergoes, from the time it enters the mouth to the time its carbon atoms become part of carbon dioxide molecules. State where in the body these changes occur.

3.1 Aerobic respiration

Key points

- Respiration provides energy for all life processes.
- Our metabolic rate can be calculated from the rate at which we consume oxygen.

- Aerobic respiration is a very similar chemical process to burning.
- We can calculate the amount of energy in food by finding how much heat it gives out when burned.

---

1 Year-7 students often confuse respiration with breathing. Design a poster to explain the differences between these two processes.

2 Tim is a year-9 student. He is revising for Key-stage 3 examinations. Tim complains that there are too many word equations to remember. Write a revision sheet for Tim, showing him the similarities between the word equations for respiration and photosynthesis.

3 Chris and John want to investigate which of their snack foods contains most energy. They set up their apparatus as shown in the diagram below.

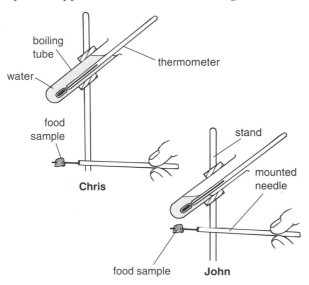

The following table shows their results.

	temperature in °C	
	at start of experiment	at end of experiment
Chris's snack food	21	70
John's snack food	24	72

a John concludes that his snack food contains most energy because it reached a higher temperature. Write a correct conclusion for this investigation.

b Chris complains that this was not a fair test. Describe how they can make this a fair test.

c Suggest a snack food that contains a high amount of energy.

---

a Write down the symbol equation for aerobic respiration.

b Energy is released during respiration. List the processes that this energy is used for.

c Explain why there are more mitochondria in muscle cells than in other body cells.

---

5 Jo set up a respirometer to measure the rate of respiration of woodlice, as shown in the diagram below.

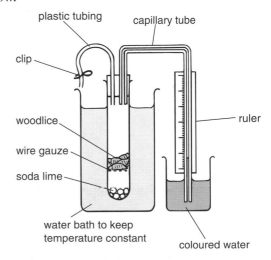

a Soda lime absorbs carbon dioxide. Explain why Jo used soda lime in this experiment.

b i Explain why the coloured water starts to rise up the capillary tube.

  ii Jo noticed that as the woodlice moved around, the coloured water rose more quickly up the tube. Give an explanation for Jo's observation.

c Explain why the tube containing the woodlice is kept at a constant temperature.

3.2 Anaerobic respiration

Key points

- Anaerobic respiration does not require oxygen.
- Different products are formed in aerobic and anaerobic respiration.

- Anaerobic respiration releases less energy than aerobic respiration.

1 Match words from the following list to each of the five equations below. You may use each word once, more than once or not at all.

- aerobic respiration
- anaerobic respiration
- fermentation
- photosynthesis

a   glucose R carbon dioxide + ethanol + energy

b   glucose + oxygen R water + carbon dioxide

c   glucose R lactic acid + energy

d   carbon dioxide + water R oxygen + glucose

e $C6H12O6 + 6O2$ R $6H2O + 6CO2$

2 The graph below shows the concentration of lactic acid in the blood of David and Nick. They did strenuous exercise for the first 15 minutes.

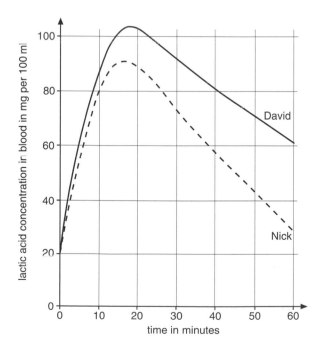

a   Which boy had the greatest concentration of lactic acid? Suggest reasons for this.

b   In whom was the oxygen debt paid off more efficiently? Suggest a reason for this.

c   Explain why the concentration of lactic acid in blood continues to increase after the exercise has stopped.

3 This extract is taken from the diary of an athlete for the day of the London Marathon.

That morning I ate a breakfast of mainly carbohydrates, with plenty of fluid. It was 3 hours before the start of the race.

The beginning of the race was crowded but we soon spread out. I kept a comfortable pace but after 15 miles my leg muscles started to ache and I felt very tired. I ran on, pushing myself through the pain for another few miles, when I suddenly became very weak and my speed dropped. I was 'hitting the wall'. I realised that my body had run out of glycogen; I had no energy reserves left. I fell to the ground, knowing I could not go on. I lay on the ground breathing deeply for several minutes. A race steward brought me a space blanket and a drink rich in carbohydrates.

Draw a cartoon strip to show each stage of the athlete's day. For each stage, write a detailed explanation of what was happening inside the athlete's body.

4 The table below shows the amount of energy released during different processes.

process	energy released in kJ per g glucose
aerobic respiration	16.1
fermentation by yeast	1.2
anaerobic respiration in muscles	0.8

a   Draw a bar chart of the information in the table.

b   Explain why least energy is produced in anaerobic respiration.

4.1 Breathing (1)

Key points

- The lungs are associated with a number of other structures that allow them to inflate and deflate.

- These structures are specialised for this particular function.

1

a In gaseous exchange, which two gases are exchanged between the environment and the organism?

b With the aid of a labelled diagram, describe the pathway of a gas from the air to the gaseous exchange surface in a human.

c Name the waste products of metabolism that are excreted through the lungs.

d State two differences, other than gaseous composition, between inspired and expired air.

2

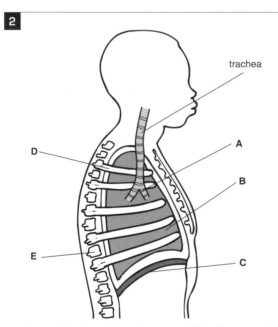

a Copy the diagram above and label parts A–E.

b Which structure separates the thorax and the abdomen?

c Which structures protect the lungs?

d Describe and explain how the trachea is kept open.

e What is pleurisy?

f Why is pleurisy painful?

3 Describe inspiration using the following six headings.

- diaphragm • ribs • volume
- pressure • air • lungs

4 The diagram below shows a model of the thorax.

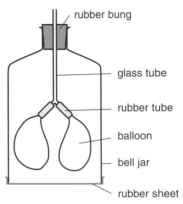

a State which structure in the thorax is represented by the following parts:
 i the rubber bung;
 ii the glass tube;
 iii the rubber tubes;
 iv the balloons;
 v the bell jar;
 vi the rubber sheet.

b Describe how you could inflate the balloons.

c Which part cannot move in the same way as the equivalent body part?

5 Copy and complete the table below to describe the functions of different parts of the breathing system.

part of breathing system	function
trachea (windpipe)	
larynx	
bronchus	
alveoli	
ribs	
diaphragm	
capillaries	
intercostal muscles	
rings of cartilage	

Continued ▶

4.1 Breathing (2)

6 The diagram below shows an apparatus for demonstrating that more carbon dioxide is breathed out than is breathed in.

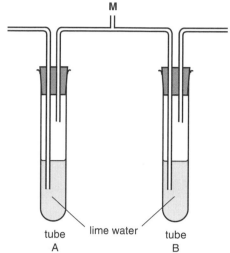

M

tube A — lime water — tube B

a Air is sucked in through M. Describe what happens in:
  i tube A;
  ii tube B.

b Air is blown out through M. Describe what happens in:
  i tube A;
  ii tube B.

c Describe and explain what has happened to the lime water in each of the two tubes after five 'suck–blow' cycles.

7 Explain each of the following changes that occurs during expiration (breathing out).

a The ribs move downwards and inwards.

b The diaphragm moves upwards. What is the diaphragm made of?

c The pressure in the thorax increases.

d Air is pushed out of the lung.

8 The table below shows the differences between inspired and expired air.

gas	percentage	
	inspired air	expired air
oxygen	20	16
nitrogen	80	80
carbon dioxide	0.04	4

a Draw pie charts to illustrate the data in the table.

b Calculate the difference in the percentage of oxygen between inspired and expired air.

c Calculate the difference in the percentage of carbon dioxide between inspired and expired air.

d Why does the percentage of nitrogen remain the same?

e Use the information above to explain why it is possible to keep someone alive using artificial (mouth-to-mouth) respiration.

9 With the aid of a labelled diagram, describe how the alveoli are adapted for gaseous exchange.

10 Breathing involves the inhalation and exhalation of gases. The apparatus shown below is used to investigate the gases exhaled during breathing.

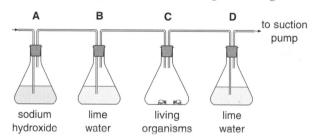

A — sodium hydroxide   B — lime water   C — living organisms   D — lime water   to suction pump

a Explain why sodium hydroxide is placed in flask A.

b Explain why lime water is placed in flask B.

c What is happening in C?

d Explain why lime water is placed in flask D.

e Why is the suction pump needed?

f Copy and complete the following table to show what you would expect to happen in flasks A, B and D, and why.

flask	change expected	explanation
A		
B		
D		

g Why would a black cloth be placed around flask C if a plant were used?

11 It is important to prevent dust, food and other foreign material from getting into the delicate alveoli. Draw a series of annotated diagrams to describe how the body achieves this.

4.2 Breathing rate and depth

- In the alveoli of the lungs, a certain amount of oxygen is removed from the inhaled air and replaced with carbon dioxide.

- This process can be adjusted according to the body's needs by altering the rate and depth of breathing.

1

a Plan an investigation to find out the effect of exercise on the rate and depth of breathing.

b Carry out your plan. (Check with an adult first.)

c Present your results clearly.

d Identify any patterns and draw relevant conclusions.

e Evaluate your investigation and suggest improvements.

2 Copy the grid below. Answer the questions and fill in the grid to find the key word.

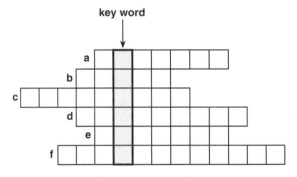

a This protects the heart and lungs.

b Gaseous exchange takes place here.

c The movement of air into and out of the lungs.

d The muscle that divides the thorax from the abdomen.

e The site where oxygen passes into the blood.

f The muscles in-between the ribs.

3 The following graph shows the number of breaths per minute for a person in three different situations.

A – breathing normal air

B – breathing pure oxygen

C – breathing a mixture of 95% oxygen and 5% carbon dioxide

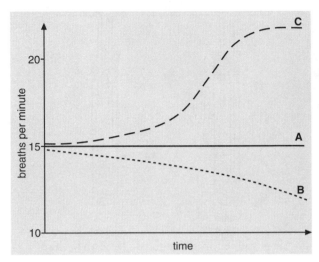

a What is the usual breathing rate in normal air?

b Describe the changes that take place in situation B. Explain your answer.

c Describe the changes that take place in situation C.

d Use your knowledge of the control of breathing to explain what is happening in situation C.

4 The table below shows the rate and depth of a man's breathing during different activities.

activity	depth in dm3 per min	rate in breaths per min
sitting	0.7	16
standing	0.8	16
walking		18
running	1.6	20

a What effect does activity have on the depth of breathing?

b What effect does activity have on the rate of breathing?

c Calculate the total air exchanged in 1 minute while the man is running.

d If air contains 20% oxygen, calculate the volume of oxygen inhaled in 1 minute of running.

e What result would you expect for the depth of breathing during walking?

4.3 Keeping the lungs clean

Key points

- The lungs have an in-built system for filtering the air and preventing infection.
- This system can be damaged by smoking tobacco.

1 The breathing system can be damaged by smoking tobacco. Smoking can have other effects as well. Some effects are obvious immediately whereas others take longer to appear. Here is a list of the effects of smoking:

- atherosclerosis • emphysema • bronchitis
- lung cancer • coronary heart disease
- arteriosclerosis • constriction of blood vessels
- ulcers • coughing • increased blood pressure
- paralysis of cilia • cerebral thrombosis
- increased pulse rate

a List the effects in a two-column table to show which appear immediately and which take longer to appear.

b Add any other effects you know of to your table.

c Find out and write about the conditions listed above.

2 The following table shows the number of deaths in 1983 from smoking-related diseases.

disease	number of deaths		
	men	women	total
lung cancer	30 000	10 000	40 000
heart attack	103 000	77 000	180 000
bronchitis and emphysema	12 000	4500	16 500

a Draw a bar chart to show the total number of deaths for each disease.

b Divide each bar into the relevant proportions to show the number of deaths in men and women.

c Explain how smoking causes:
  i emphysema;
  ii coronary heart disease;
  iii lung cancer;
  iv bronchitis.

3 The following graph shows tobacco consumption given as the average number of cigarettes smoked per adult per day.

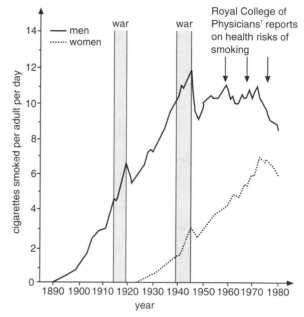

a i When did men start smoking?
  ii When did women start smoking?

b Describe the pattern of cigarette smoking shown by the whole population.

c i Describe the effect of the 1914–18 war on smoking habits.
  ii Suggest an explanation for your answer to part i.
  iii Describe the effect of the 1939–45 war on smoking habits.
  iv Suggest an explanation for your answer to part iii.

d What effect did the Royal College's reports have on the smoking pattern in:
  i men;
  ii women?

e Suggest and explain reasons for a downward trend in deaths due to lung cancer.

4

a What is passive smoking?

b Present arguments for and against the introduction of non-smoking areas in public places.

c Devise a questionnaire to investigate peoples' views on smoking.

5.1 **The green machine**

1 The diagram below shows an experiment into photosynthesis. The leaf is left in sunlight for 48 hours. It is then tested for starch.

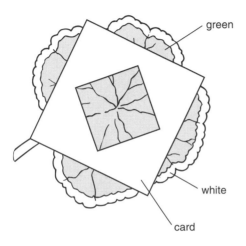

a Draw and label the leaf to show its appearance after the starch test.

b Explain your diagram.

c In another experiment the leaf was placed in a polythene bag containing soda lime. Describe and explain how the appearance of the leaf after the starch test would differ from that in part a.

d Explain how you could show that leaves give off oxygen during photosynthesis.

2

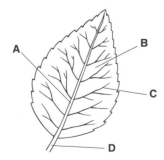

Copy the diagram above and complete labels A–D.

3 Explain the importance of photosynthesis to:

a all living organisms;

b animals;

c industry.

4 The photomicrograph below shows a stomata and guard cells in a leaf, magnified ¥ 1200.

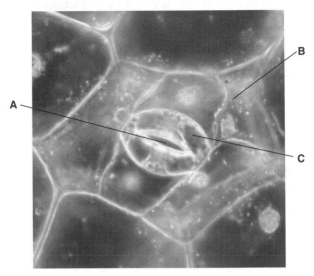

a Name the parts labelled A–C.

b Calculate the maximum length of a pore. (Don't forget to show your working!)

c Explain the mechanism involved in the opening and closing of the stomata.

5 Write an account of the pathway taken by a carbon atom in a molecule of carbon dioxide in the air until it becomes part of a starch molecule stored in a potato. Include every structure it passes through and all compounds it forms part of.

6 Draw a table to show the differences between photosynthesis and respiration.

7 The leaf is a specialised organ adapted for the function of photosynthesis.

a Describe at least six ways in which the leaf is adapted to obtain sunlight energy.

b Describe three ways in which the leaf is adapted to obtain and get rid of gases.

c Describe three ways in which the leaf is adapted to obtain and get rid of liquids.

5.2 Limiting factors

Key points

- The rate of photosynthesis is affected by changes in light intensity, temperature and carbon dioxide concentration.

- The rate of photosynthesis may be limited by conditions such as light intensity, temperature and carbon dioxide concentration.

1 The graph below shows the effect of light intensity on the rate of photosynthesis in different concentrations of carbon dioxide (CO_2).

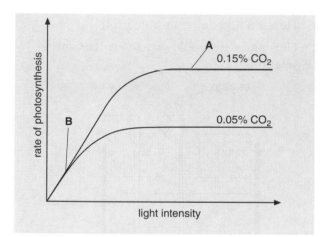

a State which factor is limiting the rate of photosynthesis at point B and explain why.

b Name one further environmental factor needed for photosynthesis that is not shown on the graph.

c Name one further substance that must be present for photosynthesis to occur.

d Suggest the factor(s) that is/are limiting photosynthesis at point A and explain how you could investigate further.

2 In any environment a factor will limit the rate of photosynthesis. For each of the environments listed below, state the most likely limiting factor, giving reasons for your answer:

a a hot desert;

b the floor of a tropical rainforest;

c the North Pole in June;

d a well-watered glasshouse in summer.

3 The following graphs show the rate of photosynthesis and the relative absorbance by chlorophyll of light at different wavelengths (colours).

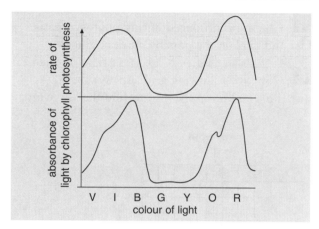

a Which wavelengths (colours) of light are absorbed by chlorophyll?

b Which wavelengths (colours) of light are reflected by chlorophyll? Explain your answer.

c The rate of photosynthesis varies. Using the data from the graphs, suggest what controls the rate.

d Explain your answer to c.

e What colour light might a horticulturalist use to illuminate his glasshouse to make his plants grow better? Explain your answer.

4 The graph below shows the carbon dioxide taken up or given off by a plant during one day.

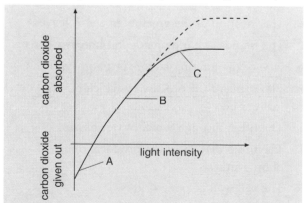

a Explain why carbon dioxide is given out at point A.

b Explain why carbon dioxide is absorbed at point B.

c Why does the curve level off at point C?

d Describe an investigation you would do to obtain the dashed line.

5.3 Photosynthesis and beyond

Key points

- Glucose is produced by photosynthesis.
- Glucose can be converted into many other substances.

- Mineral salts in the soil are required for all these processes.

1 Glucose is produced during photosynthesis. List and explain the possible fates of glucose.

2 Copy the following grid. Answer the questions and fill in the grid to find the key word.

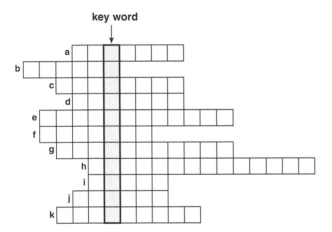

key word

a Transported in the phloem.

b The products of photosynthesis are polymerised into this.

c Energy source for photosynthesis.

d The pores through which gaseous exchange takes place.

e The location of the green pigment in leaves.

f The monosaccharide made in photosynthesis.

g One of the limiting factors in photosynthesis.

h The name of the process by which plants make food.

i The tubes through which water passes.

j The tubes that carry the products of photosynthesis.

k The cell wall is made of this.

3 Chlorosis is a condition in which leaves become yellow.

a Explain why a lack of magnesium causes chlorosis.

b Explain what would happen to the rate of photosynthesis in leaves affected by chlorosis.

4 The diagram below shows one of a series of jars set up to investigate the need of plants for various trace elements.

a Why are the jars covered with black paper?

b How would you set up a control?

c How and why would you aerate the culture solution?

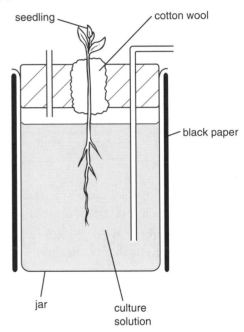

5 Copy and complete the table below, which shows the elements needed by plants.

element	ion	function of ion in plant
		made into amino acids and then proteins
	K+	
phosphorus		
	Ca2+	
magnesium		
sulphur		
	Cu2+	
manganese		

6.1 Blood circulation (1)

Key points

- The blood is carried around the body in blood vessels called arteries, veins and capillaries.

- The blood transports materials to and from the tissue fluid.

1 The diagram below represents the circulatory system of a human. Some blood vessels are labelled A–J.

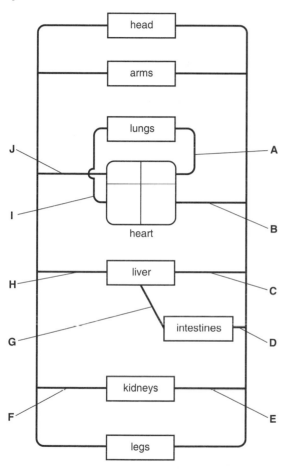

a Copy the diagram and complete labels A–J.

b On your diagram draw arrows to show the direction of the blood flow in vessels B, F, G, and I.

c Vessel I carries deoxygenated blood. Most deoxygenated blood is carried in veins. Why is this vessel an artery?

d Vessel I divides into two after leaving the heart. Explain why.

2

a The following table lists parts of the circulatory system. Copy and complete the table to show the function of each part.

names	function
artery	
vein	
capillary	
heart	

b The following are statements about the circulatory system. State whether each is true or false.

  i The circulatory system transports nutrients around the body.

  ii The circulatory system transports oxygen around the body.

  iii The circulatory system transports waste to the cells.

  iv The circulatory system transports nitrogen around the body.

  v The circulatory system transports heat around the body.

  vi The circulatory system transports hormones around the body.

  vii The circulatory system transports vitamins and minerals around the body.

c The human blood system is a double circulation. Explain what is meant by this.

d   i How does a valve function?

    ii Where in the circulatory system would you find valves?

3 Below is a list of blood vessels and a list of functions. Copy the lists, matching each blood vessel with the correction function.

blood vessels	functions
artery	carries blood to the heart
vein	allows exchange of gases
capillary	carries blood away from the heart

6.1 Blood circulation (2)

4 Copy the following grid. Answer the questions and fill in the grid to find the key word.

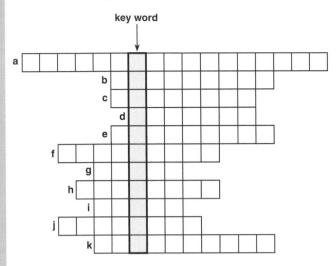

key word

a The vessel that takes blood from the small intestine to the liver.

b The component of blood pressure measured in arteries when the heart is relaxed.

c These take blood away from the heart.

d The heart is made up of this type of muscle.

e The part of the circulatory system that involves the lungs.

f The site of exchange of substances between blood and tissues.

g The pump.

h The circulation of blood through the body.

i These take blood to the heart.

j The component of blood pressure measured in arteries when the heart is contracting.

k The chambers that pump blood out of the heart.

5 David needs energy in order to play football. He gets the energy needed by his leg muscles from respiration. Respiration needs glucose and oxygen. The glucose comes from the food David eats. Once digested, the glucose is absorbed into the blood.

a List in order the parts of the circulatory system through which the glucose passes to get from the small intestine to the muscles of his leg. (The vessel supplying the leg is the femoral artery.)

b If the femoral artery were severed, the blood would come out in spurts. Explain why an artery bleeds in spurts whereas blood seeps slowly from a vein.

6 The diagram below shows a normal artery on the left and a diseased artery on the right.

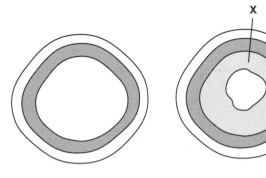

a Suggest what would be found at **X**.

b How does the deposit at **X** affect the external diameter of the artery?

c How does the deposit at **X** affect the internal diameter of the artery?

d Describe how this deposit could affect the blood flow through the artery.

e Explain you answer to **d**.

f Describe and explain how stress affects the arteries.

7 Each kidney receives blood from one artery. A vein takes blood away from the kidney. The kidney has millions of cells, each of which is supplied with blood.

a Explain what happens to the artery as it enters the kidney so that each cell receives blood and eventually only one vein leaves the kidney. Include the names of all vessels, relative sizes and functions.

b Using the following words, explain what is happening in a capillary network.

• arteriole • artery • diffusion
• high pressure • low pressure • lymph vessels
• tissue fluid • vein • venule

6.2 The heart

Key points

- The heart is a double muscular pump that pumps blood around the body and the lungs.
- This means the body has a double circulatory system.

1 The diagram below shows an external view of the heart.

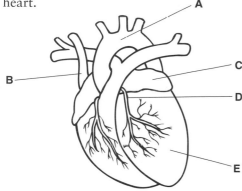

a State the names of the parts labelled A–E.

b The heart is made of muscle. Name the type of muscle.

c What is special about this muscle?

d Describe the difference between the walls of C and E.

e Explain why there is a difference between the walls of C and E.

f The heart muscle is supplied with blood by vessel D. Describe and explain what could happen if this vessel was blocked.

2 The following sentences describe the passage of blood through the heart in one complete circulation but they are listed in the wrong order. Copy the sentences in the correct order.

- The bicuspid valve prevents back flow.
- The walls of the left atrium contract, pushing the blood into the left ventricle.
- The walls of the right atrium contract, pushing the blood into the right ventricle.
- Blood is forced out of the heart into the aorta.
- The right atrium fills with blood.
- The right ventricle contracts, pushing blood into the pulmonary artery and to the lungs.
- The vena cava brings blood to the heart from the body.
- The walls of the left ventricle contract.
- The pulmonary vein brings blood back to the heart from the lungs.
- The left atrium fills with blood.

3 The heart pumps blood around the body and lungs by contraction of the muscle. Each contraction is called a beat. The heart beats throughout life. If it stops, death will follow unless the heart is restarted.

a Calculate how many times the heart of a 75-year-old person has beaten, showing your working.

b Why is the heart called a double pump?

c What is diastole?

d Name and describe the two types of systole.

e During each beat, the heart makes a 'lub-dub' sound. What is happening in the heart to make these sounds?

4 The heart rate (pulse) is the number of beats per minute. The stroke volume is the volume of blood pumped out of the heart with each beat. The cardiac output is the volume of blood pumped out of the heart each minute.

The table below shows how these three factors are linked during resting and exercising.

	at rest	while running
pulse in beats per min	70	110
stroke volume in cm^3	100	140
cardiac output in cm^3 per min	7000	

a Calculate the cardiac output while running.

b Calculate the pulse rate if the cardiac output is 10 800 cm^3 per min and the stroke volume is 120 cm^3.

c Describe and explain the effect of exercise on:
  i pulse rate;
  ii stroke volume;
  iii cardiac output.

6.3 **Blood**

Key points

- Blood transports materials around the body.
- The blood and the skin act as a defence against infection.

- Blood can clot to seal wounds and prevent the entry of microbes.

1 When blood is centrifuged (spun round at very high speed in a test tube), the heavier components go to the bottom of the tube. The test tube looks like this:

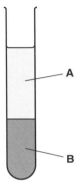

Copy and complete the table below to show the four components of blood and their functions.

test tube label	name of component	function(s)
A		
B		
B		
B		

2 The diagram below shows a sample of blood under the microscope.

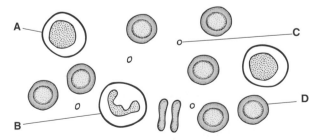

a Name the structures labelled A–D.

b Describe the function of each of the structures A–D as part of the blood.

c Where are red blood cells made?

d Where are white blood cells made?

3 Blood transports substances around the body. Copy and complete the table below to give the relevant information for as many substances as possible.

substance	where picked up	where released

4 The red blood cells carry oxygen.

a Explain how the oxygen in the air taken into the lungs is absorbed, carried and delivered to the cells of the body.

b Why are red blood cells red?

c Explain why red blood cells have no nucleus.

5 Sometimes patients in hospitals receive a blood transfusion.

a What is a blood transfusion?

b Why might a patient need a blood transfusion?

c Find out and write ten facts about donating blood.

d Research the major ways of grouping blood. Write a report to present to the rest of the class.

6 There are about 5 million red blood cells in 1 cubic millimetre (mm^3) of blood. An adult has about 5 litres of blood. Red blood cells last about 120 days, after which they are broken down and replaced.

Calculate the following, showing your working:

a the total number of red blood cells in an adult;

b the percentage of red blood cells that are replaced each day.

7 Find out and write about the following disorders of the blood:

a leukaemia;

b haemophilia.

8 William Harvey helped to find out about blood. Write down ten facts about Harvey.

6.4 Water transport in plants (1)

Key points

- Water enters root hairs by osmosis.
- It travels up the stem through the xylem vessels.
- Stomata close at night to minimise water loss.

1 Copy the following grid. Answer the questions and fill in the grid to find the key word.

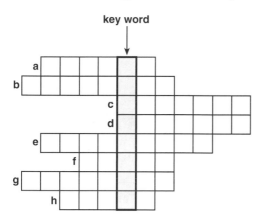

key word

a A method of transport across membranes in cells.

b Water is taken in here.

c Water leaves the leaf through these.

d This layer of leaf is waterproof.

e Water passes across the cell wall by this process.

f The vessels through which water passes.

g These substances, e.g. phosphorus, can be taken up with water.

h These cells control the opening and closing of the leaf's pores.

2 The diagram below shows the detail of part of a root and some soil particles.

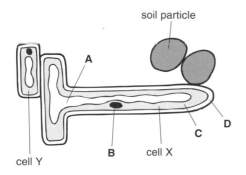

a Copy the diagram and complete labels A–D.

b How is cell X adapted for the function it performs?

c State the name of the process by which water passes from the soil to cell Y.

d Give a detailed explanation of this process in the cells shown.

e Which feature of the cell membrane is important for this process?

f Name one other substance that might be taken in with the water.

g Name the structure that transports water from the root to the stem.

3 The diagram shows a white carnation. After one day the left side of the flower is red.

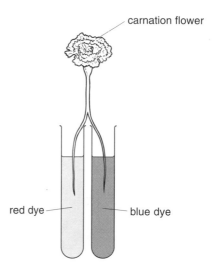

a Explain how the colour gets from the test tube to the white petals.

b i What colour would the right side of the flower be?

   ii Explain your answer to i.

6.4 **Water transport in plants (2)**

4 The diagram below shows a cross-section of a leaf.

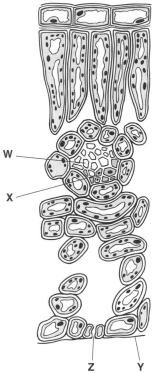

a State the names of the structures W–Z.

b Explain how these structures:

   i enable water loss to occur;

   ii prevent too much water loss occurring.

5 The diagram below shows detail of various parts of a plant that are involved in the transport of water.

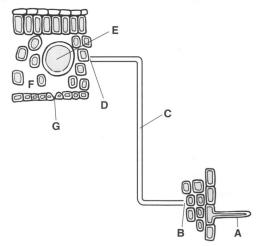

a Copy the diagram and draw in arrows to show the path of water movement.

b Explain what is taking place at each of the points A–G.

6 The diagram below shows a xylem vessel.

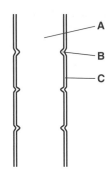

a Copy the diagram and complete labels A–C.

b How are the cells labelled B formed?

c **i** What is C impregnated with?

   ii What effect does this have?

d On your diagram:

   i label the top of the plant;

   ii label where you think the root is;

   iii draw an arrow to show the direction of water movement.

---IDEAS AND EVIDENCE---

7 Hooke used a microscope to see cells. Find out and write about Hooke's work.

6.5 Transpiration

Key points

- Transpiration pulls water up the stem.
- Environmental factors influence the rate of transpiration.

- Sugars move up and down the stem through living phloem vessels.

1 The diagram below shows a cutting in a pot of soil covered by a polythene bag.

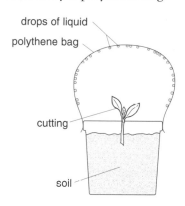

drops of liquid
polythene bag
cutting
soil

a Name the liquid you would expect to see on the inside of the bag.

b How would you test this liquid?

c Where has this liquid come from?

d This liquid would only appear if the height of this cut stem is less than 10 metres. How does liquid get to the top of a tree that is 100 m tall?

2 The graphs below show information about transpiration.

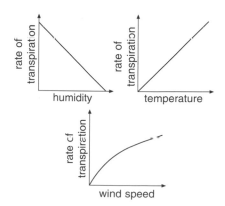

a With reference to the graphs, describe the relationship between the rate of transpiration and:

i humidity;
ii temperature;
iii wind speed.

b Explain how light might affect transpiration.

3 The potometers below show pieces of a plant in different conditions.

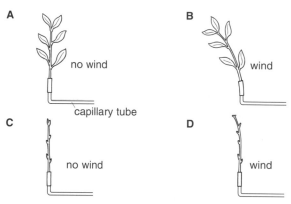

A no wind
B wind
capillary tube
C no wind
D wind

a How could you measure the uptake of water using this apparatus?

b i In which potometer would the uptake of water be fastest?
ii Explain your answer to i.

c i In which potometer would there be no water movement?
ii Explain your answer to i.

d Name one other factor that affects transpiration rate and describe how you would modify/use this apparatus to show its effect.

4 Aphids pierce the stems of plants to obtain substances they need.

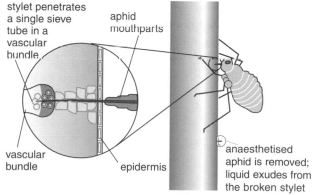

stylet penetrates a single sieve tube in a vascular bundle
aphid mouthparts
vascular bundle
epidermis
anaesthetised aphid is removed; liquid exudes from the broken stylet

a Name the tissue that the aphid targets.

b What substance is the aphid trying to obtain?

c Explain why the aphid pierces this tissue.

7.1 Distribution of organisms

Key points

- The terms habitat, population and community can be used to describe where and in what combinations organisms live.
- Organisms are not spread out at random where they live but prefer certain areas.

- Various methods can be used to map the distribution of organisms in their environment.

1 As Lucy stared into the rock pool, six small fish darted towards the clump of seaweed and two tiny crabs crawled under a rock. Clinging to the rock were four sea anemones, their tentacles swaying in the clear water. Lucy counted eight prawns as they moved over the sandy floor. She tried to catch one with her hands, making sure her fingers did not touch the sea urchin.

a List the different populations in the rock pool and their numbers.

b Use the example above to explain the difference between a habitat and a community.

c Describe a different type of habitat that Lucy might have seen in this area.

2 Copy the lists below, matching each organism with its habitat.

organisms	habitats
frog	leaf litter
trout	marine rocky shore
lichen	pond
millipede	desert
sponge	river
cactus	wall

3 Steven noticed that duckweed had started growing on the surface of his garden pond. Every 2 days he counted the number of plants. His findings are shown in the following table.

day	duckweed
1	1
3	9
5	33
7	91
9	125
11	131
13	133

a Plot the data in the table as a graph.

b Describe how the population of duckweed changes with time.

c Suggest reasons for this change in population.

4 Tim's dad said that only grass would grow on the football pitch because of people constantly walking on it. Tim said that people walk on their lawn and that weeds grow on the lawn as well as grass. Tim's theory is that the weeds that grow on their lawn will also grow on the football pitch. Tim wants to carry out an investigation to compare the plants growing on the lawn and the football pitch. Describe an investigation Tim could do to support his theory

5 Some year-6 primary-school pupils want to study the organisms in their environment. Design a set of leaflets that explain how to use the following sampling techniques:

a quadrats;

b line transects;

c pitfall traps;

d tree beating;

e sweep nets;

f pooters.

6 A group of students was asked to measure the population of beetles in the school garden. On the first day the students caught 34 beetles in their pitfall traps. They marked each beetle with a spot of paint. On the second day they caught 21 beetles, 8 of which had spots painted on them.

A formula called the Lincoln index can be used to work out the total number of beetles in the area:

$$\text{total number of animals} = \frac{A \times B}{C}$$

where A is the number of animals marked and released in the first sample, B is the total number of animals captured in the second sample and C is the number of marked animals in the second sample.

Use the Lincoln index to calculate the total size of the beetle population.

7.2 Competition and adaptation

> ## Key points
>
> - The number of organisms in a habitat is often affected by competition from other organisms.
> - Organisms tend to be adapted to live in a particular habitat.

1 The diagram below shows some features of a dandelion plant.

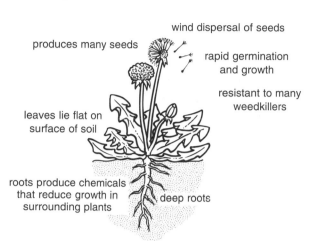

- wind dispersal of seeds
- produces many seeds
- rapid germination and growth
- resistant to many weedkillers
- leaves lie flat on surface of soil
- roots produce chemicals that reduce growth in surrounding plants
- deep roots

Explain how each of the features helps to make the dandelion an excellent competitor.

2 Living organisms compete for resources. Make a list of the resources that each of the following organisms needs to compete for:

a cress seedlings;

b otters;

c owls.

3 Living organisms have to be adapted to their habitats in order to survive.

a Copy the table below but match each organism with its adaptations.

organism	adaptations
flounder	small spines for leaves, water storage inside stem, long roots
cactus	hibernates through the winter months
dormouse	migrates south for winter
swallow	can change colour to match its background

b Describe the habitat for each organism in the table above.

4 The diagram below shows some arrowleaf plants grown in different habitats.

A damp soil **B** shallow still water **C** deep fast-moving water

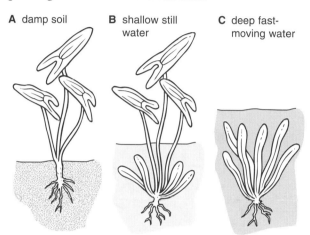

Explain how each of these plants is adapted to survive in its habitat.

5 Some mink escaped from a farm in Staffordshire. The following year the otter population was found to be in decline. Local conservationists said that this decline was caused by the escaped mink. Explain why the conservationists had reached this conclusion.

6 The diagram below shows Farmer Ted's crop of corn growing close to a hedge.

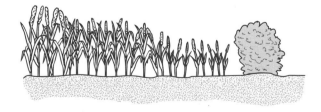

Farmer Ted wonders why the corn close to the hedge does not grow as well as the rest of the crop. Write an explanation for Farmer Ted.

IDEAS AND EVIDENCE

7 Farmer Ted considers removing the hedge. Suggest advantages and disadvantages for Farmer Ted for the removal of hedges.

7.3 Predation and co-operation

Key points

- Predators are animals that catch and eat other animals, called prey.
- If large numbers of these predators survive in a habitat, the number of prey will go down.
- Instead of eating each other, other types of organisms work together and some may rely completely on each other.

1 Jane collected this leaflet from her local health centre.

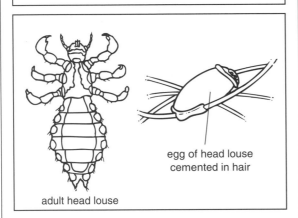

HEAD LICE

egg of head louse cemented in hair

adult head louse

The head louse is an insect which lives on the scalp. The hair provides the ideal place to lay eggs: the temperature is just right and food is plentiful. To feed, the louse bites the scalp and sucks blood.

The female louse lays about six eggs during the night, sticking each one to a separate hair with a kind of glue. Young lice hatch out after 1 week, leaving behind an egg case still glued to the hair.

a Write down the name of the type of relationship between the head louse and its host.

b Explain how the head louse obtains its food.

c Explain how the head louse is adapted for its habitat.

2 Lord McDuall owns an island. He decided that there were too many rabbits on the island, so he introduced weasels to feed on the rabbits. Soon there were too many weasels. Lord McDuall invited hunters to shoot all the weasels. A few years later there were so many rabbits that they were competing for the grass. Many rabbits starved.

a Explain why the hunters were wrong to shoot all the weasels.

b Draw a predator–prey graph to illustrate the changes in the populations of rabbits and weasels.

3 Sam the gardener noticed some aphids on his tomato plants. A few days later there were lots more aphids. Sam did not want to use a pesticide so he put some ladybirds on the plants. The ladybirds ate the aphids. When there were few aphids left, the ladybirds flew away. Soon after Sam noticed more aphids, so he put some more ladybirds on the plants. This information is represented in the following predator–prey graph.

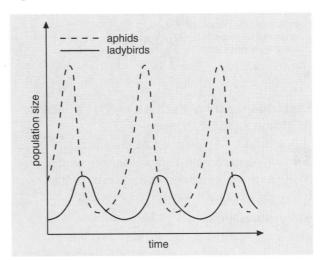

a Suggest why Sam did not want to use a pesticide on his plants.

b Write down the two populations represented by the graph.

c Explain the changes shown in these populations.

d Continue the graph to show what might have happened if the ladybirds had not flown away.

e Describe another predator–prey relationship that would show similar changes in populations.

4 Explain the differences between the following pairs of terms:

a mutualism and parasitism;

b host and prey;

c population and community.

7.4 Food chains and energy

Key points

- Pyramids of biomass are a useful way to describe food chains.
- Food chains can also be thought of as showing the flow of energy through a community.
- This flow of energy can be used to explain various properties of food chains such as the shapes of pyramids of biomass.

1 Below is the pyramid of numbers for a wooded community.

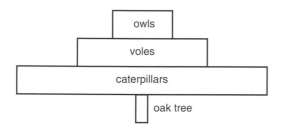

a Draw a pyramid of biomass for this wooded community.

b What is meant by biomass?

c Explain why a pyramid of biomass provides a more accurate representation than a pyramid of numbers.

d Describe how biomass is calculated.

e What do scientists use pyramids of biomass for?

2 The diagram below shows the energy transfer at one stage of a food chain.

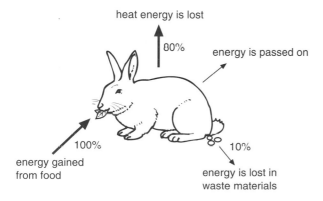

a Describe how most energy is lost at this stage of the food chain.

b What percentage of energy will be passed on to the carnivore?

c Explain how some of the energy stored in the waste materials is released.

d Explain why most food chains are short.

3 Below are three common food chains:

A green plants → human

B green plants → lamb → human

C green plants → insects → fish → human

a State which food chain has the greatest energy loss. Give a reason for your answer.

b Discuss the issue being debated in the cartoon below, stating the advantages and disadvantages. Finish with your own opinions.

4 This is an extract taken from an advertising leaflet.

THE SCOTTISH MOORS

The main types of vegetation are heather and grass. These may grow to a height of 0.5 m. The heather and grass provide food for grouse. The moors are also home to small mammals such as voles. These also feed on the heather and grass. The main predators are foxes, which feed on both the grouse and the voles. During the hunting season, you can enjoy our traditional grouse casserole.

a Draw a food web for the organisms mentioned in the leaflet.

b Choose a food chain from your food web and draw a pyramid of biomass to represent it.

c Suggest what else the heather and grass provide for the grouse in addition to food.

7.5 Decomposition and recycling

Key points

- Decomposers feed on dead organisms and organic material that is given out from food chains.

- To work properly, these organisms need the correct conditions.
- This is the first step in recycling all the elements back into the environment.

1 Some Year-8 students read about the carbon cycle whilst researching acid rain. Design a poster for the Year-8 class to explain the carbon cycle. Your poster should be interesting, colourful and informative.

2 Below is a diagram of the carbon cycle. Copy the diagram into your book and fill in the processes X, Y and Z.

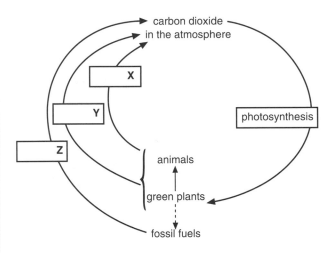

a How is carbon removed from the air?

b Millions of years ago green plants changed into coal.
  i Describe how the carbon in coal becomes carbon dioxide in the air.
  ii What environmental problem does this carbon dioxide cause?

c Some people say that the carbon cycle is like an oxygen cycle in reverse. Explain what is meant by this.

3 Imagine a biological disaster that caused all the decomposers to be destroyed. Describe your journey into school.

4 Some Year-10 students did an investigation to discover which conditions caused the fastest rate of decay in a compost heap. Each group of students was given the same amount of degradable material and their compost heaps were set up in the science laboratory as follows.

- Group 1 used a plastic airtight container. They sealed the lid and left the container in the light.
- Group 2 used a wire-mesh container. They stirred and watered the material once a week and left the container in the light.
- Group 3 copied group 2 but put their container in a dark cupboard.
- Group 4 used a cardboard container with holes punched in the side and the top. They watered their material once a week.
- Group 5 used a wire-mesh container, they stirred and watered their material twice a week. They put their container next to the heater.

a Draw a results table for the Year-10 students' compost heaps and predict their results.

b Plot a bar chart to show their results.

c The students did not understand why decomposition took place at different rates. Write a conclusion for their experiment.

d Write an evaluation of this experiment.

5

a Joe is a Year-11 student revising for his exams. He thinks that plants take in nitrogen from the air. Use the nitrogen cycle to explain to Joe how plants obtain the nitrogen they need.

b Copy and complete the following table.

type of bacteria	function
nitrogen fixing	
	break down nitrates to release nitrogen gas
nitrifying	

c Explain why crop rotation is beneficial to farmers.

7.6 Food production (1)

Key points

- The human population is increasing, which means that more food is needed.
- Knowledge of energy flow in food chains can be used to make food production more efficient.

- Various pests try to eat our food and various methods are used to try to stop them.

1 Rothamsted Experimental Station researched the effect of fertilisers on crop yield. Their findings are shown in the table below.

plot	conditions	yield in kg per hectare
1	no manure or chemical fertiliser	800
2	farmyard manure	2200
3	chemical fertiliser with all minerals	2500
4	chemical fertiliser with no magnesium	2100
5	chemical fertiliser with no phosphorus	1600
6	chemical fertiliser with no nitrogen	900

a Plot a bar chart of these results on graph paper.

b Which fertiliser produced the highest yield?

c Which element had the most effect on the yield? Give a reason for your answer.

2

a Copy the table below and complete it by writing in the correct key word from the list for each description.

- fungicide
- herbicide
- insecticide
- rodenticide

key word	description
	chemicals that kill weeds; also known as weedkillers
	chemicals used to poison rats, mice and other rodents
	chemicals that kill tiny organisms called fungi, which grow on seeds, plants or harvested crops
	chemicals used to kill insect pests; small aeroplanes are often used to spray these chemicals over large fields

b Suggest why each of these chemicals might be used.

3

A PRICKLY POSITION

A few years ago, Australian farmers were plagued by wallabies which ate their crops. To keep the wallabies out, the farmers planted the prickly pear cactus (*Opuntia*) around the edges of their properties. The prickly pear grew very well so that it not only kept the wallabies out, but is now spreading into the fields and choking the crops. Crop yield is now even lower than before.

a What result were the farmers expecting to achieve by planting prickly pear?

b Explain what went wrong with this plan.

c Suggest a biological method that will control a foreign species of weed.

4 The diagram below shows what happens when fertiliser gets into a lake. This process is known as eutrophication.

1. farmer adds fertiliser to the land

2. fertiliser drains through soil and into water

3. fertiliser causes the plants (including the surface algae) to grow faster

4. surface algae stop sunlight from reaching the plants lower down in water

5. plants unable to photosynthesis and die

6. decomposition process uses oxygen out of water

7. fish die due to lack of oxygen

a Describe the process of eutrophication in your own words.

b Local fishermen thought that the fertiliser had poisoned the fish. Write an information leaflet for fishermen, explaining why the fish died.

c Suggest other substances that could cause eutrophication.

Continued ▶

7.6 Food production (2)

5 Farmyard manure contains humus, which improves soil quality. Chemical fertilisers do little to maintain good soil structure. They also lead to water pollution.

a Study this information and the table in Question 1. Can we support the large-scale use of chemical fertilisers? Write a report for farmers, including as much information as possible to support greater use of organic manure.

b Suggest other ways that farmers use to increase food production.

c A scientist wrote, 'Increasing food production is not the answer to the world's problems, we need to look at the bigger picture'.

   i What do you consider to be the 'bigger picture'?

   ii If you were a government minister, what reforms would you impose?

6 In the late 1950s, the number of peregrine falcons decreased suddenly. The table below shows the results of a survey.

year	number of breeding pairs of peregrine	
	non-farming areas	farming areas
1940	500	280
1960	460	90

a Draw a bar chart to show the data in the table.

Another observation made in the 1950s was that dead pigeons were often found near fields which had been planted with wheat seed. From the 1940s, farmers used to soak wheat seed in an insecticide called dieldrin in order to prevent the seeds from being eaten by the wheat bulb fly.

b Write a conclusion from these two sets of results.

The scatter graph below shows the eggshell index (relative weight) of peregrine eggs from 1900 to 1960.

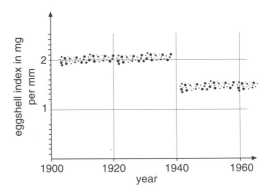

c In which year was there a drastic reduction in the eggshell index?

d Imagine you are the Minister for Agriculture. Write a report based on these sets of information.

7 In her book *Silent Spring*, Rachel Carson (1907–64) wrote about the excessive use of chemicals in pest control, 'These insecticides are not selective poisons: they do not single out the one species of which we desire to be rid'. Write about your views on this comment.

7.7 Energy and waste

Key points

- With the increasing world population, there is a great demand for energy.

- Producing this extra energy produces a number of waste products that have caused serious pollution.

1 Jamie's great-grandfather has heard about the greenhouse effect. However, he says that he does not understand it and that it never happened in his day.

a Draw a poster for Jamie's great-grandfather to explain how the greenhouse effect is caused.

b Jamie's great-grandfather is 95 years old. Do you think the greenhouse effect occurred in his younger days? Give reasons for your answer.

c Jamie's great-grandfather wants to know what the greenhouse effect will do to our world. Write an account of the changes that might take place if the greenhouse effect is not reduced.

2 Lichens are easily damaged by sulphur dioxide gas in the air. The table below shows the number of lichen species found at various distances from a city centre.

distance from city centre in km	number of lichen species
0	1
2	4
4	8
6	14
8	20
10	12
12	20
14	29

a Plot a graph of the data in the table on graph paper.

b Describe the pattern shown by the results.

c A motorway passes the city. From your graph suggest the distance of the motorway from the city centre. Give a reason for your answer.

d Write down one other harmful effect that sulphur dioxide has on our environment.

IDEAS AND EVIDENCE

3 The table below shows the levels of lead found in Greenland snow strata (layers).

year	concentration of lead in snow in parts per billion
1750	0.01
1800	0.03
1825	0.05
1850	0.04
1875	0.05
1900	0.07
1925	0.08
1950	0.12
1975	0.22

a Plot a graph of the data in the table on graph paper.

b Explain why scientists went all the way to Greenland to take readings from the snow strata.

c Suggest a reason for the gradual increase in lead pollution from 1750 to 1930.

d Explain why there has been such a steep increase since 1930.

e Suggest how lead pollution can be harmful to humans.

4 Environmentalists have suggested that power stations are the real cause of acid rain. Prepare your part for a class debate on the following motion: 'There will be a global rise in the cost of electricity. This will allow those countries responsible for producing the gases that cause the acid rain to pay compensation to those countries affected by the acid rain.'

7.8 **Conservation**

- The increasing population of the world and their demand for resources is causing the destruction of habitats and organisms.

- There are many reasons why we should try to stop this. Many conservation projects are underway throughout the world.

1 Describe the difference between a **protected species** and an **endangered species.**

2 The diagram below is taken from an information leaflet about recycling.

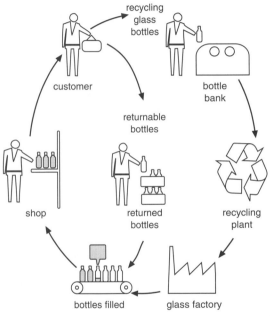

recycling glass bottles

customer

returnable bottles

bottle bank

shop

returned bottles

recycling plant

bottles filled

glass factory

a List the stages involved in recycling glass bottles.

b Describe the difference between recycling and re-using.

c Write down the name of one other material that is commonly recycled.

d Explain why it is important to recycle materials.

3 The Countryside Commission established a set of rules to help protect the environment of the National Parks. The rules are called The Country Code. They include:

- Take your litter home.
- Guard against all risk of fire.
- Keep to public paths.
- Fasten all gates.
- Help to keep all water clean.

Design a leaflet or poster that the Countryside Commission could display to explain how The Country Code protects wildlife.

4 The graph below shows changes in the population of protected elephants in Zimbabwe over a 9-year period.

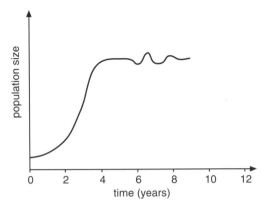

Make a sketch of this graph.

a Label with an X where the birth rate and death rate are equal.

b Label with a G to show where the population was growing without limits.

c A drought affected the water supply. The water became polluted and the elephants started to die at a faster rate. Complete your sketch of the graph to show this change in population.

IDEAS AND EVIDENCE

5 Following the United Nations conference *The Law of the Sea* in the 1970s, the North Sea was divided into sectors. Each country was given the right to use the resources of its own sector.

a Suggest why the North Sea was divided into sectors.

b Explain how the mesh size of fishing nets and the use of fishing quotas help to conserve fish stocks.

6 Many adults are unaware of the need for conservation. Design an information leaflet to describe some of the methods of conservation. These should include methods such as conservation areas, gene banks, captive breeding programmes and conservation laws.

8.1 Detecting stimuli

Key points

- Receptors detect different stimuli and convert the information into nerve impulses.

- The retina of the eye contains many light receptors. The eye also has a number of other structures that help to focus the light so that a clear image can be formed.

1 Key-stage 3 students often have difficulty learning the names and the order of the different parts of the nerve process.

- **stimulus** • **detection** • **co-ordination** • **response**

Copy the words onto pieces of card to make a jigsaw. The different parts of the process must only fit together in the correct order.

2 Your eyes automatically control the amount of light that enter them. Work with a partner. Ask your partner to sit with their head tilted back, looking towards a light. Stand close to them so you can look down into their eyes. Ask your partner to close their eyes for a few minutes. When they open their eyes, watch the size of the pupil.

a Write down your observations.

b Explain why the eye does this.

3 Copy the following diagram of a section through an eye.

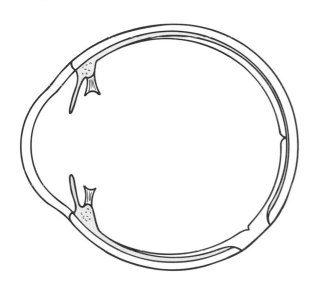

a The lens and the optic nerve are missing from the diagram above. Add them to your diagram.

b Add the following labels to your diagram:

- **blind spot** • **ciliary muscles** • **cornea** • **fovea**
- **iris** • **lens** • **optic nerve** • **pupil** • **retina**

c On your diagram show light rays entering the eye and coming to a focus.

d Describe how the light rays are brought into focus.

e Explain why we have a blind spot.

f Use the diagram below to find your blind spot.

Hold this page about 50 cm from your face. Close your left eye and concentrate on the cross with the right eye. Slowly bring the page closer to your face. When the image of the dot falls on the blind spot, it will seem to disappear.

4

a Write down the five senses.

b Write down the parts of your body that are involved with the detection of each of the five senses.

c Explain how your sense of smell can help to protect you.

5 During an eye test Judy was asked to read the letters on a wall chart. The optician then asked Judy to read from the book she was holding. As Judy looked from the wall to the book, it was a few seconds before she could focus on the book.

a Describe the change that was taking place to the lenses in Judy's eyes.

b Why does this change take place?

c Explain how this change was brought about.

6 As Justine and Alex were walking home in the dark, Justine noticed that she could see the cars passing, but could not make out their colour unless they drove under the light of a street lamp. Explain why Justine and Alex can see the cars in the dark, but are unable to determine their colour.

8.2 Nerves

Key points

- Information is sent around the body as nerve impulses in special cells called neurones.
- These neurones are specialised so that they can carry out this job efficiently.
- Synapses allow impulses to pass between neurones and can be affected by various drugs.

1 The following words/terms are often confused:

- nerve • neurone • nerve impulses

a Explain the differences between these words/terms.

b Year-9 students have difficulty with the words/terms listed in part **a**. Write a paragraph for a Year-9 class, describing how information is sent around the body. Make sure you include the words/terms listed.

2 Make a three-dimensional model to represent a nerve. Materials you might use include drinking straws, string or wool, a cardboard tube or an empty plastic bottle. For your next lesson be ready to explain each part of your model to others in the class. Your model will make part of a class display.

3 Year-9 students have difficulty understanding the structure of neurones. Draw a neurone on a piece of card and make a learning jigsaw for a Year-9 student. Add labels, then cut it out. Make sure the pieces only fit together in one way.

4 Explain how the structure of the neurone helps it to carry out its function efficiently.

5 Jane overheard some adults discussing alcohol. She thinks that the adults do not really understand about the effects of alcohol on the body. Explain why each of the following statements is **NOT** true.

a I drink alcohol when I am working late because it is a stimulant drug.

b I only drink beer because it is less harmful than drinking spirits.

c Drinking heavily for several years does not harm you because your body gets used to it.

d It is safe to drive if your blood alcohol concentration is just below the legal limit.

6 Mr Jones met his clients at 1.00 p.m. They each had a glass of wine before leaving the office. During lunch, Mr Jones drank two glasses of wine and a brandy. Mr Jones and his clients returned to the office at 2.30 p.m. to complete their deal. Mr Jones left the office at 6.00 p.m. On his way home he met some friends and they each drank two pints of beer. At 7.30 p.m. Mr Jones decided to take a taxi home. The graph below shows the level of alcohol in Mr Jones's blood from lunchtime.

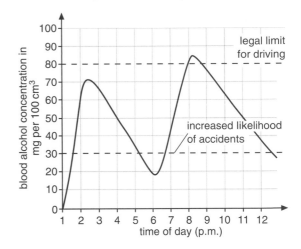

a Was it necessary for Mr Jones to take a taxi home in the evening? Explain your answer.

b From your graph state the time when:
  i Mr Jones was most likely to have an accident at work;
  ii his blood alcohol level was highest.

c Suggest what time Mr Jones's blood alcohol level would have returned to zero:
  i that night;
  ii if he had not drunk any beer.

7 Neurones are not connected directly to each other. Between the projections from two neurones are minute gaps. These are called synapses.

a Explain in detail how impulses pass across a synapse.

b Expain how drugs can affect synapses.

8.3 Co-ordination and response

Key points

- Nerve impulses are sent from receptors to the central nervous system (CNS) along sensory neurones.
- The CNS co-ordinates all the information from the receptors and brings about a response. This may be a reflex or a voluntary action.
- Nerve impulses are then sent to the effectors along motor neurones.

1 Christine has put her hand into hot water. The diagram shows what happens in the nervous system.

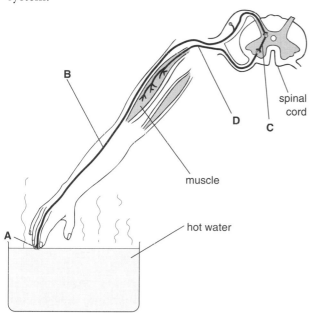

a Copy the diagram and complete labels A–D. Choose your labels from this list.

- motor neurone • pain sensor
- relay neurone • sensory neurone

b On your diagram label:
  i the effector;
  ii the stimulus.

c Describe the response.

d On your diagram draw circles to show where synapses can be found.

e Add arrows to your diagram to show the direction in which the nerve impulses travel.

f Write down the name given to this pathway of nerve impulse.

g Is the action shown in the diagram an example of a monosynaptic response or a reflex action? Give a reason for your answer.

2 Copy the following table into your book. Complete the table by filling in the missing key words and meanings.

key word	meaning
	the pathway along which nerve impulses pass in a simple reflex action
reflex	
	process by which sensory information is monitored and responses initiated for the benefit of the organism as a whole
spinal cord	
	part of the nervous system, consisting of the brain and spinal cord
relay neurone	

3 Describe the similarities and differences between sensory neurones and motor neurones.

4 Year-9 students studying the nervous system often become confused and include the brain in the reflex action.

a Write an illustrated account of a reflex action for a Year-9 class. Explain why the nerve impulse does not travel immediately to the brain.

b Write a question to test Year-9 students on their understanding of the information you have given them. You need to include a marking scheme that clearly shows where marks are awarded so that they can mark each other's answers.

8.4 **Hormones**

- Hormones are chemical messengers carried around the body in the blood.

- They are produced by various ductless glands in the body and are an alternative to communication by nerves.

1

a Make a poster to show the human hormonal system. Draw the outline of a human body onto a large sheet of plain paper. (If you have some old wallpaper you could make it life-size.) On your outline draw diagrams of the glands that secrete hormones.

b Write about the functions of each hormone and add this information to your poster.

2 Make a learning game for Year-9 students. You will need some blank cards. Write the names of hormones on some of these cards, on others write the functions of the hormones, and on others write the names of the hormone-secreting organs.

To play the game, mix the cards together and share the cards out beween the players. Each person places a card face up on a central pile. If the card you place on the pile is linked to the one below (for example, pancreas and insulin), shout 'hormone' and pick up the pile of cards. The person with most cards at the end is the winner.

3

a List four ways in which the hormonal system differs from the nervous system.

b Explain how the hormones get into the blood.

c Explain the role played by the liver as part of the hormonal system.

d i Write down the name of the gland that produces insulin.

  ii Describe the function of insulin.

4 A scientist once said, 'The pituitary gland is the conductor of the orchestra of hormones'. Explain what the scientist meant by this statement.

5 Two hormones that are prepared commercially are insulin and progesterone. Describe the uses of these two hormones.

6 The graph below shows the levels of glucose and insulin in a person's blood over a 12-hour period.

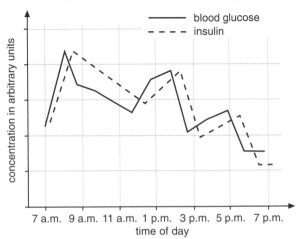

a i At what times did this person eat their meals?
  ii Give reasons for your answer to **i**.

b Explain why the concentration of insulin rises and falls.

c Diabetics do not produce enough insulin and therefore need to inject insulin into their bodies. Use the graph above to explain why a single daily dose of insulin would not control blood glucose levels adequately.

d Diabetics inject insulin before breakfast and before their evening meal. Sketch a graph to show the blood glucose level and insulin level in a diabetic person over a 24-hour period.

e A diabetic person injected insulin at breakfast, then went for a jog. He ran further and faster than intended. On his return he measured his blood glucose level and found that it was too low. Explain what had happened in his body to cause the blood glucose level to fall too low.

7 During PHSE lessons Year-7 students are taught about adolescence and how their bodies will change during puberty. The word hormone is often used in these lessons. Design a poster for Year-7 classrooms to explain what is meant by the word hormone. Include information on how hormones will affect the students' lives during their next few years.

8.5 The role and use of hormones

Key points

- Physical changes that occur during adolescence are controlled by sex hormones. These hormones are produced by the sex organs.

- In females, the menstrual cycle is controlled by oestrogen, progesterone, and hormones from the pituitary gland.
- We now use hormones medically to control fertility. Hormones may be used illegally by some sporting competitors.

1

a Write down the name of the female hormone produced by the ovaries at puberty.

b Describe the changes this hormone causes to a girl's body.

c Write down the name of the male hormone produced by the testes at puberty.

d Describe the changes this hormone causes to a boy's body.

2 Explain why urine tests are used to find out if a woman is pregnant.

3 The graph below shows how the thickness of the uterus lining changes over a period of time.

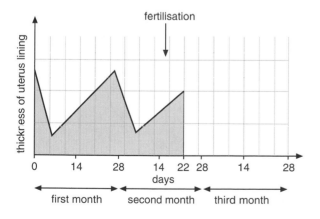

a Copy the graph. On your graph draw a line labelled menstruation to show when the uterus lining was lost.

b How many days did menstruation continue for?

c How many days after menstruation did ovulation occur?

d Describe the role of progesterone in the menstrual cycle.

e Fertilisation occurred on the 16th day of the second menstrual cycle. Complete your graph

to show what happens to the lining of the uterus after day 22 in the second month.

f Explain why it is important for the lining of the uterus to change in the ways shown.

4 Occasionally a woman's oviduct (Fallopian tube) can become blocked. This means that she cannot have a baby in the normal way, but she may be able to have a 'test-tube' baby. The doctor pushes a fine tube through the body wall and takes several eggs from the ovary.

a Suggest what could be done to ensure that the woman produces many eggs.

b Explain why the eggs cannot be obtained through the vagina and uterus.

c Some of the eggs are frozen and the rest are put into a dish. Suggest why some of the eggs are frozen.

d Sperm are mixed with the eggs in the dish. After a few days the developing embyros are put into the woman's uterus through the cervix.

  i Explain why sperm are mixed with the eggs before they are put into the woman's uterus.

  ii Explain why the embryos are kept for a few days before they are put back into the woman's uterus.

5 The process described in Question 4 is called *in vitro* fertilisation.

a Draw labelled diagrams to explain the process of *in vitro* fertilisation.

b Some people think that *in vitro* fertilisation should not be paid for by the National Health Service. Discuss this issue, stating the advantages and disadvantages. Finish with your own opinions.

8.6 Response to stimuli in plants (1)

Key points

- Plants usually respond to stimuli by growing in a particular direction.

- These growth responses are usually controlled by plant growth substances or hormones.

1 Draw a poster for Year-7 students to show how plants respond to various stimuli. Include several colourful drawings on your poster. Keep the writing to a minimum and include only a few technical terms.

2 Explain how tropic movements help plants to live successfully.

3 Mrs Fry, the school cook, left some potatoes in a cupboard but left the rest in the vegetable rack near the kitchen window. After the school holidays Mrs Fry noticed that the potatoes had begun to sprout, but the potatoes left in the dark cupboard had longer sprouts than those left in the vegetable rack. Write an explanation for Mrs Fry.

4 Explain the difference between tropic and nastic movements.

5 Copy the grid below. Answer the questions and fill in the grid to discover the key word.

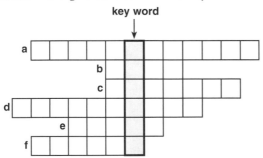

key word

a A growth response in plants either towards or away from a light source.
b Auxins are produced in the tip of a shoot and pass back to an area behind the tip where they cause cells to _____.
c Positive phototropism describes the response in which shoots grow _____ the light.
d A growth response in plants either towards or away from gravity.
e A plant hormone that is produced at the growing points.
f A growth response by plants to a non-directional stimulus.

6 The diagrams below show an experiment to investigate the effects of auxin on a plant.

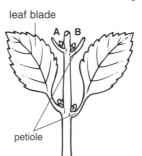

leaf blade

petiole

leaf blades removed at **A** and **B**

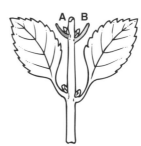

petiole **A** coated with an auxin in petroleum jelly;
petiole **B** coated with petroleum jelly only

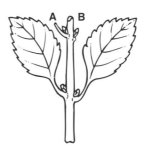

after a few days petiole **B** has fallen off

a Explain why petiole B was treated with petroleum jelly that did not contain auxin.

b Scientists think that leaf fall might be controlled by the plant. Use information from the diagrams to support this idea.

c A gardener wrote to *Gardening News*. He had noticed that when he trimmed his hedge, which removed the shoot tips, more side branches started to grow out of the main stem. He wondered why this happened. Write a letter of explanation to the gardener.

Continued ▶

8.6 Response to stimuli in plants (2)

7 The diagrams below show three plant stems, X, Y and Z, at the start and end of an experiment.

X

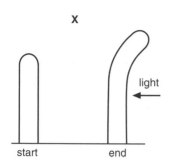

start   end   light

Y

opaque cap

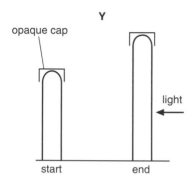

start   end   light

Z

opaque sleeve

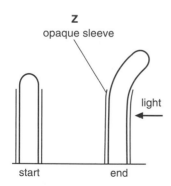

start   end   light

a Write a conclusion for this experiment. Suggest which region of the plant stem is sensitive to the stimulus of light, giving reasons for your answer.

b Explain what causes the plant stem to bend towards the light.

c Suggest how this response is beneficial to the plant.

8 The physics teacher, Mr Lane, complains that he has to keep turning the plants on his windowsill. He does not seem to realise that the plants are growing towards the light.

a Write a simple explanation of how a plant is able to move towards light when placed on a windowsill.

b Explain why this ability is useful to the plant.

9 Design a board game to illustrate plant growth responses for students of your own age. Bring it to the next lesson. Exchange your game with someone else's. Play their game and write an evaluation of the game.

(Some hints: label the top of the board 'away from gravity'; label the foot of the board 'towards gravity'; label the sides 'towards/away from light'. Draw squares on the board. Make a spinner with four sides, labelled positively phototropic etc. Use a dice to show the number of squares to move. Add extra statements into some of the boxes.)

10

a Auxins are produced by the developing seed embryo. The auxins control ripening by instructing the ovary to develop into a fruit. Explain how seedless grapes are produced.

b Ethene is produced by many fruits. It causes the fruit to ripen. Explain how ethene can be used to regulate the ripening of fruit during transport.

8.7 Uses of plant hormones

- Plants produce a number of growth substances that control all aspects of their growth and development.

- We can use many of these substances to try to change the way in which plants grow.

1 Copy the grid below. Answer the questions and fill in the grid to discover the key word.

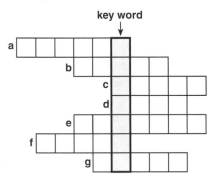

key word

a
b
c
d
e
f
g

a Auxins stimulate rapid _____ of shoots.

b Auxins stimulate the growth of _____ from the base of stems or leaves.

c Ethene is made by many fruits – it causes the fruit to _____.

d Auxins make the shaded side of the plant grow more, so the plant _____ towards the light.

e Geo_____ and photo_____ are responses of plants to gravity and light, respectively.

f The name given to the plant hormone.

g Synthetic auxins are used to kill _____.

2 Copy the following statements, filling in the missing words.

- Plant growth and development is controlled by _____ .

- Rooting powders contain synthetic _____. The powder stimulates the cut shoots to produce _____.

- Weedkillers also contain _____ auxins. They kill weeds by making them _____ too _____.

- To develop seedless fruit farmers spray the _____ _____ on _____ flowers and the fruits form without _____. These fruits have no _____.

3 Draw a large poster to show the uses of plant hormones. Include rooting powder, weed killers, the production of seedless fruits and the ripening of fruit.

4

HARRY'S ROOTING HORMONE

GUARANTEED

IT'S ROOTS AHEAD OF THE REST

GET STRAIGHT TO THE ROOT

Below are the instructions from a container of rooting powder but they are in the wrong order.

- Remove the lower leaves.
- Water, then place pot in a plastic bag.
- Cut off a shoot of new healthy growth, making your cut diagonally.
- Plant into a small pot of compost.
- Dip cutting into rooting powder.
- Dip cutting into water.

a Sort out the instructions and write them out in the correct order.

b Suggest why the lower leaves should be removed.

c Explain what the hormone in the rooting powder does to the cutting.

d Write down the name of the hormone found in rooting powder.

e The rooting powder also contains a fungicide. Suggest why this is necessary.

f Explain why the cutting needs to be watered, then placed inside a plastic bag.

5 While shopping with her mother, Jenny bought some seedless grapes. She also noticed there were seedless satsumas.

Jenny has learnt about sexual reproduction in plants at school but does not understand how the fruit can be grown without seeds. Write a letter to Jenny explaining how seedless fruits can be grown.

9.1 Controlling glucose levels

Key points

- Homeostasis means maintaining a constant internal environment in the body.
- It involves keeping the body's levels of glucose, water and metabolic waste unchanged.

- The hormone insulin is involved in homeostasis, keeping the level of glucose constant.

---

1 Copy and complete the passage below by filling in the missing words. The passage is about controlling blood sugar level.

After a meal, there is too much glucose in the blood. The _____ makes and releases the hormone _____. It is released into the _____ and transported to its target organ, the _____. Here it causes excess _____ to be changed into _____ and the level of blood glucose _____.

---

2 The graph below shows the changes in blood glucose level in a normal person after eating a meal rich in carbohydrates.

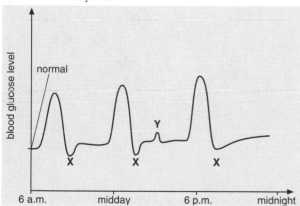

a **i** Describe the pattern shown in the graph.
   ii Suggest reasons for the pattern.

b **i** Suggest a reason for the fall in blood glucose level at the three points marked **X**.
   ii What could have caused the slight increase in blood glucose level at point **Y**?

c **i** What is diabetes?
   ii Sketch the graph of blood glucose level against time (24 hours) for a person with untreated diabetes.

d How is negative feedback involved in the homeostatic control of blood glucose level?

---

3 Glucose is the product of the digestion of carbohydrates. It is found in the small intestine when digestion is complete.

a Explain what is happening to the glucose at stages 1–5 in the flow diagram below.

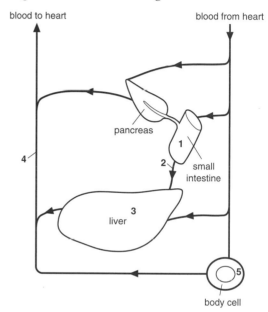

b The pancreas secretes the hormone insulin.
   i What stimulates the production of insulin?
   ii How does insulin lower the blood glucose level after a meal?
   iii What stops the blood glucose level from falling too low?
   iv What is the normal blood glucose level (in mg per 100 ml blood)?

4

a **i** Describe two symptoms of diabetes.
   ii Explain how the disease causes these symptoms.

b Some diabetics have to inject insulin whereas others (often older people) can control their blood glucose level by diet alone.
   i Why are there these two types of diabetes?
   ii Describe how someone might change their diet to control their diabetes.
   iii Explain you answer to part **ii**.

c Because insulin is a protein, it must be injected into the body in order to avoid digestion by enzymes in the digestive system. Name an enzyme that could digest insulin.

9.2 Controlling temperature (1)

Key points

- The skin is an important organ in temperature control.
- Changes in body temperature can prevent enzymes from working.
- The skin controls temperature by sweating and by regulating the flow of blood near the surface.
- H Cells in the brain detect the core temperature of the body and control the skin's temperature-control mechanism.

1 A class of GCSE students measured their temperatures in °C. Their results are shown in the table below.

student	body temperature in °C
Clare	37.6
William	36.8
Lawrence	37.1
Nicola	37.2
Peter	36.9
Nicholas	37.4
Sally	37.2
Stephen	37.0
Matthew	39.5
Rasheed	38.0
Susan	36.5
Tina	36.7
Nicolle	37.4
James	37.1
Robert	35.2
Fay	37.0
Kirsty	38.0
Salma	37.2
Wendy	37.0
Dominic	36.8

a Calculate the average temperature.

b What pattern can you see in the results?

c List the anomalous results and suggest an explanation for them.

d One member of the class is very pale. How might this be explained in terms of temperature regulation?

2 The diagram below shows a cross-section through the skin.

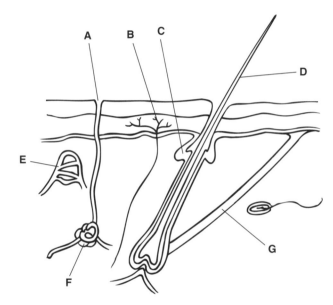

a Copy the diagram and complete labels A–G.

b Explain in detail how the following are involved in keeping the skin cool:
  i   structures A and F;
  ii structure E;
  iii structures D and G.

3 Normal body temperature is 37°C. It is important to maintain this temperature. If the body temperature rises or falls, the body can bring it back to normal using homeostatic mechanisms.

a State three mechanisms by which the body reduces its temperature when too hot.

b State three mechanisms by which the body increases its temperature when too cold.

c Drinking cold drinks can reduce the body temperature. Explain how.

Continued ▶

9.2 **Controlling temperature (2)**

4 Copy the following grid. Answer the questions and fill in the grid to find the key word.

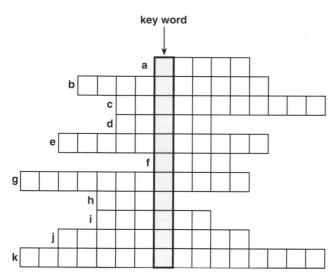

key word

a These can stand on end to trap air to keep you warm.

b Sweat _____ to reduce body temperature.

c This is normally 37°C.

d Liquid released onto the surface of the skin when hot.

e This is used to measure a person's temperature.

f This structure covers your whole body.

g The term given to an animal which cannot control its body temperature.

h A toxic substance in sweat and urine.

i A structure that carries blood.

j When the body is too hot the capillaries do this.

k The process in the capillaries when the body is too cold.

5 Animals have a variety of ways to keep warm or cool (control their temperature). Explain how the following animals try to regulate their temperatures:

a a dog;

b a polar bear;

c seals and whales;

d birds.

6

a During illness the body temperature can rise to 41 or 42°C. The homeostatic mechanisms cannot always bring the body temperature down to normal. Explain what effect these high temperatures could have on the body's metabolism.

b Draw a flow diagram to show how parts of the body are involved in regulating the temperature. (Include the skin and the brain.)

c Some animals, for example dogs, have other mechanisms for controlling temperature.
  i Why does a dog pant with its mouth open?
  ii Explain how the fur on a dog's body helps the animal to keep warm.

7 Some animals can control their body temperature whereas others cannot.

a State the word that is used to describe animals that can control their temperature.

b i State the word that is used to describe animals that cannot control their temperature.
  ii How is the temperature of these animals controlled?

c The graph below show the body temperature of a human and a crocodile at different environmental temperatures.

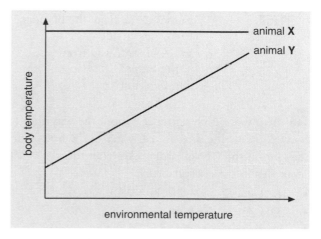

i Which line represents the human? Explain your answer.
ii Which line represents the crocodile? Explain your answer.

9.3 Kidneys and lungs (1)

Key points

- The kidneys ensure that urea, excess water and excess salt are removed from the body.

- The lungs ensure that carbon dioxide is removed from the body.

1 The diagram below shows the position of the kidneys and other associated structures in the body.

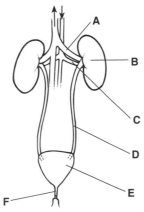

a Copy the diagram and complete labels A–F.

b Below is a list of the parts labelled in the diagram and a list of their functions. Copy the list of the structures and write the correct function alongside each.

structures	functions
kidney	brings blood to the kidney
renal artery	passes urine from the kidney to the bladder
renal vein	
ureter	stores urine
bladder	passes urine from the bladder to the outside
urethra	
	takes blood away from the kidney
	filters blood

2 Below are nine sentences about the way the body controls the amount of water in the body but they are in the wrong order. Copy out the sentences in the correct order.

- The level of water in the blood increases.
- ADH enters the kidneys.
- Less urine is produced.
- There is not enough water in the blood.
- The hypothalamus detects the shortage of water.
- ADH is released.
- More water is reabsorbed.
- The urine becomes more concentrated.
- Nerve impulses are sent to the pituitary gland.

3 Copy and complete the grid below.

across

2 fluid excreted from the body

3 stores urine

4 maintenance of a constant internal environment

5 toxic substance made by the liver

6 associated with the kidney

9 takes urine to the outside

10 fluid found on the skin

down

1 filters blood

2 tube that takes urine from the kidney to the bladder

4 the type of substance (e.g. ADH) that controls the water balance of the body

7 released by pituitary gland

8 used in breathing

4 The following diagram shows an alveolus and its blood supply.

a Explain what is taking place at each of the points A–F.

b i The wall of the alveolus is very thin. How does this help gaseous exchange?

Continued ▶

9.3 Kidneys and lungs (2)

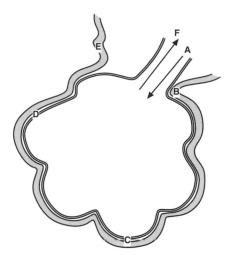

ii How does the good blood supply to the alveolus help to maintain a concentration gradient for gaseous exchange to occur?

iii List the other features of the lungs/alveoli that help to make gaseous exchange efficient.

5 The table below shows a comparison of the contents of blood and urine.

	concentration in grams per 100 cm³	
substance	urine	blood
water	96	90
protein	0	9
urea	2	0.03
ammonia	0.04	0.001
glucose	0	0.1
sodium ions	0.6	0.3
chloride ions	0.6	0.3

a Name the substances that are excreted.

b Which substances are present in blood plasma at a higher concentration than in urine?

c Explain why the substances referred to in **b** do not usually appear in the urine.

d Where is urea made and from what?

e What substance would you find in the urine of a diabetic that would not be found in the urine of a healthy person?

6 The following table shows the volumes of sweat and urine produced at different air temperatures.

air temperature in °C	sweat produced in cm³ per hour	urine produced in cm³ per hour
0	4	100
5	4	90
10	9	78
15	22	64
20	40	54
25	62	42
30	100	30
35	200	20

a Plot a graph of the data in the table on one pair of axes.

b Describe the changes in the volume of sweat as the air temperature increases.

c Explain why the volumes of sweat and urine change when air temperature changes.

7 Sometimes kidneys fail to function adequately. The person could either have a transplant or undergo dialysis.

a Explain what a transplant is. In your explanation include information on where the kidney comes from, how the kidney is matched and why antibiotics and anti-rejection drugs are needed.

b There are two types of dialysis. Find out about each type and prepare a leaflet about dialysis aimed at young people with kidney failure.

IDEAS AND EVIDENCE

8 Some people who have kidney failure need to use dialysis. This treatment is very expensive. More than half of the patients use dialysis at home. About a quarter of patients with kidney failure receive kidney transplants. Some patients receive no treatment at all.

A kidney transplant operation costs £9000 and the drugs cost a further £3500 per year. Dialysis costs £16 000 per year in hospital or £14 000 per year at home.

a Explain why only one quarter of patients with kidney failure can have transplants.

b Prepare a discussion document for a hospital board meeting showing why it is cheaper for hospitals to perform kidney transplants rather than treating patients using in-hospital dialysis.

10.1 Genes and chromosomes – 1

Key points

- The nucleus contains threads of DNA called chromosomes.

- Chromosomes are divided into sections called genes. Genes carry instructions and may be copied and passed on to the next generation.

1 Make a model of a chromosome. Materials you might use include wire or strong thread, different coloured Plasticine or sweets. Bring your model to the next lesson and be prepared to explain your model to the rest of the class. Then use your model as part of a display.

2

a Estimate the length of DNA from one person.

b Suggest why the DNA needs to be so long.

c Explain how such a long length of DNA can fit inside the nucleus of a cell.

3 Copy the table below and complete it by filling in the missing key words and meanings.

key word	meaning
	the molecule that codes for all the instructions needed to make an organism, and is also capable of replication
genes	
	structures composed of DNA and found in the nuclei of cells
nucleus	
	the four chemicals A, B, C and G that code for the instructions of life on DNA

4 Miss White, the science teacher, says that the plant on the windowsill has 12 pairs of chromosomes.

a How many chromosomes are there in the nucleus of a root cell?

b How many chromosomes are there in the nucleus of a pollen cell?

c Explain why the number of chromosomes in the gametes is different from the number of chromosomes in all other cells.

d If Miss White made a comparison between the chromosomes found in the nucleus of a root cell and those in the nucleus of a leaf cell, what would she find? Give reasons for your answer.

e Write down the two functions of DNA.

5 The diagram below shows part of a DNA molecule.

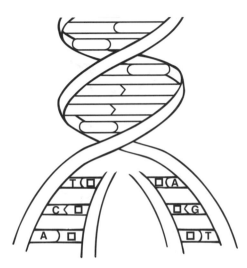

a Copy the diagram and complete it by writing the letters of the missing bases in the boxes.

b Write yourself a revision note that will help you to remember that the bases A and T always pair together and that C and G always pair together.

c Explain why each person (except for identical twins) has a unique set of DNA.

6

a Describe the structure of DNA in your own words. Illustrate your answer with a simple diagram.

b Draw a flow chart to show the stages in making a protein.

IDEAS AND EVIDENCE

7 In 1962 Crick, Watson and Wilkins received the Nobel Prize for their work on the structure of DNA. Explain why their work in determining the structure of the DNA molecule was so important.

10.2 Genes and chromosomes – 2

Key points

- Each species of organism has a specific number of chromosomes in the nucleus.
- Humans have 46 chromosomes (23 pairs) in each nucleus.

- The chromosomes that determine sex are called the X and Y chromosomes.

---

1 The diagram below shows the formation of human sex cells.

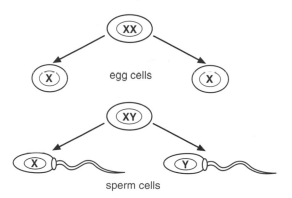

a How many chromosomes are there in the gametes (sex cells)?

b Explain why there are no Y chromosomes in the egg cells.

This diagram shows fertilisation.

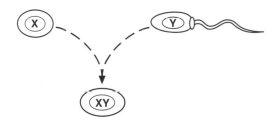

c How many chromosomes are there in the zygote (fertilised egg cell)?

d Will the baby be a boy or a girl? Give a reason for your answer.

e Draw a Punnett square to show the probabilities of having a boy or a girl.

f On rare occasions things go wrong and the zygote may contain: XXY, XXX or XYY. Describe the problems that may be associated with these combinations of sex chromosomes.

---

2 The diagram below shows the chromosomes from the body cell of a person with Down's syndrome.

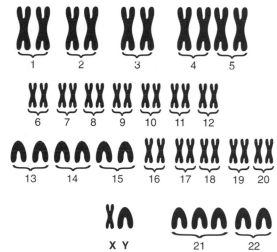

a Describe how these chromosomes are different from those from a person who does not have Down's syndrome.

b Down's syndrome occurs because of an irregularity that takes place during the development of an egg in the mother's ovary.
  i Describe this irregularity.
  ii Explain what happens at fertilisation to produce a person with Down's syndrome.

c Are the chromosomes in the diagram from a male or a female? Explain your answer.

IDEAS AND EVIDENCE

3 Henry VIII wanted a son to be king after him. It is claimed that he divorced his first wife, Catherine of Aragon, and executed his second, Anne Boleyn, because they gave him daughters. His third wife, Jane Seymour, did have a son. Henry thought that the mother determined the sex of the baby.

Imagine you are a solicitor defending Catherine of Aragon. Prepare your defence speech to support the fact that Catherine was not responsible for giving birth to a daughter.

10.3 Variation – the causes (1)

Key points

- Variation within a species can be caused by the environment, by genetics, or by a combination of both.
- Some genetic variation arises from mutations.

- Mutations can be caused by faulty copying of the gene, or by environmental factors that damage the gene such as harmful chemicals and radiation.

1 Copy the table but matching each key word with its correct meaning.

key word	meaning
DNA	changes that happen to the chromosomes or the sequence of the chemical bases
inherited	differences that exist between organisms
mutations	passed from parent to child via the genes
variation	the molecule that codes for all the instructions needed to make an organism, and is also capable of replication

2 Draw a table with three columns, with the headings: 'environment', 'genetics', and 'combination'. List five characteristics in each column.

3 Occasionally two normal-coloured parents will produce an albino offspring. Albinos have no coloured pigment in their skin, fur/hair or eyes. Albinos occur in all animal groups, and occasionally in plants.

a Only one in thousands of offspring is an albino. Suggest the difficulties this might cause an animal such as a lion.

b Suggest any examples where being an albino could be an advantage for an animal.

c Parts of a plant may have no pigmentation. Explain why a plant that was completely albino would not be able to survive.

4 Copy the grid below. Answer the questions and fill in the grid to discover the key word.

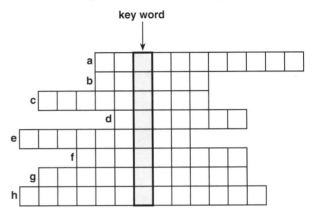

a Some variation, such as intelligence, height and weight, is thought to be the result of a _____ of inherited and environmental factors.

b Mutations can be caused by _____ copying of the gene.

c Differences that exist between organisms.

d Some variation is inherited from _____.

e Passed from parent to child via the genes.

f Certain chemicals and _____ can damage the DNA and change the sequence of the bases.

g Structures composed of DNA and found in the nuclei of cells.

h Characteristics such as hair length and a scar are _____ variation.

Continued ▶

10.3 Variation – the causes (2)

5 The diagram shows a faulty section of a DNA molecule.

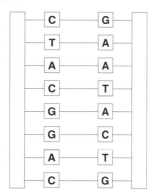

a Copy the diagram and circle the faulty part.

b Draw a diagram to show the correct appearance of this section of DNA.

c State the term given to a change caused by faulty DNA.

d Write down two possible causes of an increase in the normal rate of faults in DNA replication.

e Explain how a change in the DNA structure can cause a cell to form a different protein.

f List the four types of mutation. Describe each of the different types of mutation.

6 On rare occasions changes occur in the chromosomes or the sequence of chemical bases. This is called a mutation and is usually a change for the worse.

In the case of Queen Victoria, one of her alleles for blood clotting changed so that it could not instruct the production of one of the blood clotting factors. The family tree below shows the effect of this mutation when it was passed on to her children, grandchildren and great-grandchildren. Two of her great grandchildren bled to death after accidents.

a Write down the sex of the great-grandchildren who bled to death.

b How did Queen Victoria pass haemophilia on to her son Leopold?

c How many of Queen Victoria's grandchildren had haemophilia?

d Explain why some of the women in the diagram are referred to as carriers.

IDEAS AND EVIDENCE

7 H. J. Muller (1890–1967) was awarded the Nobel Prize in 1946 for his work on the use of x-rays to increase mutation rates.

a Describe how radiation and certain chemicals can cause mutations.

b State an example of a condition caused by a mutation.

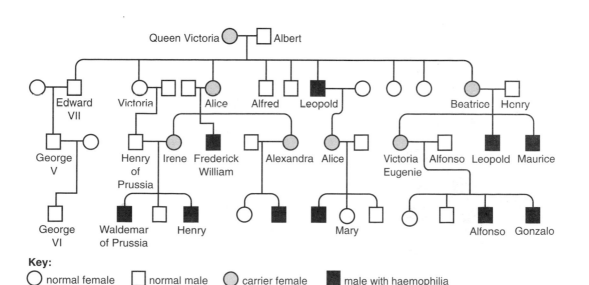

Key:
○ normal female   □ normal male   ⬤ carrier female   ■ male with haemophilia

10.4 Variation – the consequences

Key points

- Most mutations are harmful but on rare occasions they may be useful.
- Some mutations can be inherited and passed from generation to generation.
- Sexual reproduction also produces variation.

1 Copy the statements below, choosing the correct word from each pair in brackets.

- Mutations are caused by (changes/similarities) in the (chromosomes/cells).
- Mutations occur by (chance/planning).
- Most mutations are (harmful/beneficial).
- Some mutations can be inherited and passed from generation to generation if they are (harmful/beneficial).
- Sexual reproduction produces (variation/no variation).

2 Mutations can occur in bacteria. Bacterial cells reproduce very rapidly, perhaps as often as once every 20 minutes. Thus a mutation, even if it occurs only rarely, is likely to appear in a large population of bacteria. Mutations in bacteria often produce resistance to drugs. The diagram below shows how mutation in bacteria can lead to drug resistance.

a Explain how one mutation can quickly result in a population of drug-resistant bacteria.

b Explain why a population of drug-resistant bacteria could be harmful to humans.

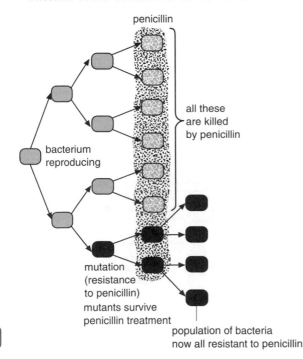

IDEAS AND EVIDENCE

3 Sickle-cell anaemia is a disease of the blood and can be fatal. It is caused by a faulty gene. The gene causes the red blood cells to be C-shaped instead of round.

a   i What causes sickle-cell anaemia?
   ii Write down the types of cells that are affected in sickle-cell anaemia.

People who carry the sickle-cell gene are resistant to malaria. This is because the malarial parasite spends part of its life cycle in red blood cells. The parasite cannot survive in the 'sickled' red blood cells. The malaria parasite is carried by mosquitoes.

The maps below show some information about mosquitoes and sickle-cell genes in Africa.

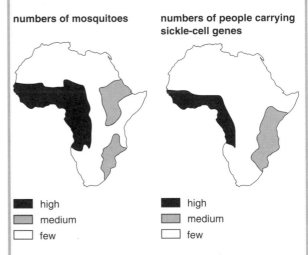

numbers of mosquitoes

numbers of people carrying sickle-cell genes

■ high
▨ medium
□ few

■ high
▨ medium
□ few

Use the information to help you write a detailed account of how the sickle-cell mutation can be considered beneficial.

10.5 Reproduction

Key points

- Sexual reproduction is a source of genetic variation – all the offspring are different.

- Asexual reproduction is not a source of genetic variation – it produces identical copies called clones.

1 Year-7 students understand that there are 46 chromosomes in the nucleus of each cell in the human body. However, they often have difficulty understanding why there are only 23 chromosomes in the nuclei of sperm cells and egg cells.

a Design a game that will help Year-7 students to understand this.

b Make your game and try it out with a Year-7 class.

2 Inside the nuclei of our cells are chromosomes.

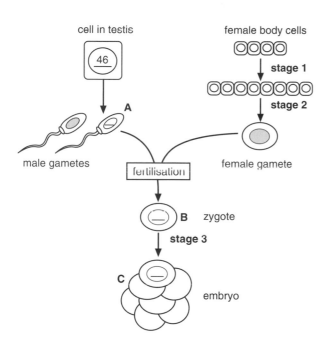

a Copy the diagram and write in the number of chromosomes inside the nucleus of the three cells labelled A, B and C.

b Write in the type of cell division, either meiosis or mitosis, at stages 1, 2 and 3.

3

a Explain how sexual reproduction brings about genetic variation.

b Explain why this is not true in the case of identical twins.

IDEAS AND EVIDENCE

4 The diagram below shows the process of tissue culture by taking leaf cuttings.

The leaf was removed from a fully grown plant that was about 9 cm tall, with pale green leaves and a dark-green stem.

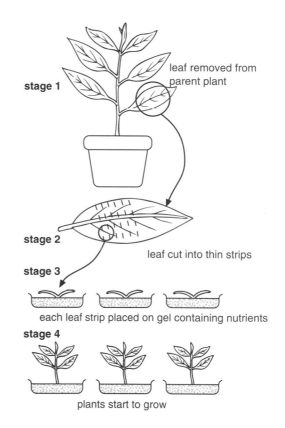

a Explain why only a small strip of leaf was needed at stage 3.

b The plants were put into compost and most of them grew successfully. Describe the appearance of the plants when fully grown.

c This is an example of micropropagation. Suggest why commercial growers prefer to grow plants by this method rather than from seed.

d These young plants are referred to as clones. Explain what is meant by the term clone.

10.6 Manipulating genes

1 *The Black Tulip* by Alexander Dumas is a novel about someone who tries to breed a black tulip. Make up your own story about a person who tries to breed a new plant or animal. Include the techniques that would have to be used and any problems that might arise.

2 A farmer grows two different crops. Each crop has desirable traits. The wheat (*Triticum*) has a high yield. The rye (*Secale*) has a high protein content and is very hardy.

The farmer selectively breeds a new crop plant that combines the desirable traits. He calls the new plant *Triticale*.

a Write down the traits of *Triticale*.

b Describe the selective breeding process used by the farmer to develop his new plant.

c Explain why this process takes many years.

d Suggest other properties that a farmer may wish to selectively breed into his crop plants.

e Give an example of how animals have been selectively bred.

3

a Give two ways in which selective breeding of plants or animals can be useful.

b Suggest one possible disadvantage of the selective breeding of plants and animals.

4 Mark is diabetic – his pancreas does not produce enough insulin. Mark needs to inject insulin into his body twice a day.

For many years this insulin has been extracted from the pancreases of cattle, sheep and pigs. Scientists can now produce human insulin using genetic engineering.

The following diagram shows some of the stages involved in the production of genetically engineered human insulin.

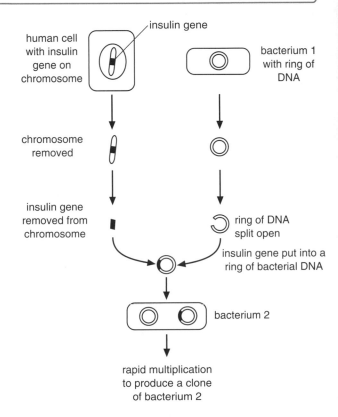

a Describe how the insulin gene is removed from the human chromosome.

b The clone of bacterium 2 produces large quantities of insulin.
  i What is a clone?
  ii Explain why bacteria are suitable organisms to use for this purpose.

c Explain the advantages of genetically engineered insulin compared with insulin extracted from animals.

IDEAS AND EVIDENCE

5 Some people are against genetic engineering. Prepare for a class discussion. Research and write about the advantages and disadvantages of genetic engineering. Finish with your own opinions.

10.7 Genetic crosses

Key points

- Genes can be dominant or recessive.
- A cross between a dominant gene and recessive gene will give a ratio of 3:1 for the dominant and the recessive traits.

1 Copy the table below and complete it by filling in the missing key words and meanings.

key word	meaning
	a description of the two alleles that form a gene
dominant	
	a genetic instruction received from one parent
phenotype	
	an allele that does not express itself in the phenotype unless two are present

2 Copy these sentences, choosing the correct word from each pair in brackets.

a A mouse with a brown-fur (genotype/phenotype) could have a BB or Bb (genotype/phenotype).

b A brown-furred mouse with genotype BB is (homozygous/heterozygous) dominant.

c A brown-furred mouse with genotype Bb is (homozygous/heterozygous) dominant.

d A white-furred mouse with genotype bb is (homozygous/heterozygous) recessive.

3 Geraniums are easy to grow, and produce red or white flowers. The allele for red flowers (R) is dominant to the allele for white flowers (r).

A red-flowered geranium (RR) was cross-pollinated with a white-flowered geranium (rr). The seeds produced by this cross were grown to produce an F1 generation of plants, all of which had red flowers.

a Explain why all the F1 generation had red flowers. Draw and complete a Punnett square to help you with your explanation.

b Two of the F1 red-flowered plants were cross-pollinated. The resulting seeds were grown to produce an F2 generation. Use a Punnett square to help you explain the genotypes and phenotypes of the F2 plants.

c Explain how you would obtain only white-flowered geraniums.

4 Chromosomes occur in pairs in all body cells.

a Explain what is meant by the term allele.

b Explain why there are two alleles for each character.

c Explain what is meant by dominant and recessive alleles.

5

a Explain the difference between **heterozygous** and **homozygous**.

Use **T** for tongue-roller and **t** for non tongue-roller.

b i Draw a Punnett square to show a heterozygous cross.

   ii Write down the ratio of possible genotypes and phenotypes.

c i Draw a Punnett square to show the genetic cross between a homozygous dominant and a homozygous recessive.

   ii Write down the ratio of possible genotypes and phenotypes.

d State the genotype and phenotype of the children if both parents were homozygous recessive. Explain your answer.

6 In these genetic crosses **B** stands for the brown-eyes allele and **b** stands for the blue-eyes allele.

a Write down the possible combinations of alleles a brown-eyed person could possess, explaining your answer.

b Draw a Punnett square for each of the following genetic crosses. For each one state the ratio of possible genotypes and phenotypes.
   i BB × bb
   ii BB × Bb
   iii bb × Bb
   iv Bb × Bb

10.8 Mendel and family trees

Key points

- Gregor Mendel was a monk who investigated inheritance by doing experiments with garden peas.

- Later, when science appreciated the data that he collected, his efforts led to an understanding of modern genetics.
- Mendel's laws of inheritance can be used to work out the genotypes of organisms.

1 Tim keeps pet mice. Use the following information to draw a family tree for Tim's family of mice. Use **A** for normal fur colour (grey) and **a** for albino characteristics.

Both parents carry a recessive gene for the albino characteristics. In the first set of offspring (F1) there were 3 grey mice (2 male and 1 female) and one albino mouse (female). The albino mouse and one of the grey mice were mated and produced 3 grey mice (2 female and 1 male) and 3 albino mice (all male).

2 The diagram below shows the inheritance of hair colour in a family. The gene for brown hair is dominant (**B**) and the gene for blonde hair is recessive (**b**).

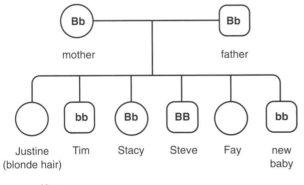

Key:

○ female   ▢ male

a State whether each of the following statements is true or false, giving reasons for your answer.
  i Stacy and Steve both have blonde hair.
  ii Stacy and Steve have different coloured hair.
  iii Stacy and Steve have the same coloured hair.
  iv All the males in the family have brown hair.

b Write down the sex and hair colour of the new baby.

c i What is Justine's genotype for hair colour?
  ii Give a reason for your answer to i.

d Fay has an identical twin. Fay has brown hair.
  i Write down the name of Fay's identical twin.
  ii Give a reason for your answer to i.

e If the mother had the genotype BB, how would this affect the genotype and phenotype of the children? Use a Punnett square to support your answer.

IDEAS AND EVIDENCE

3 Mendel worked with pea plants. Each flower of a pea plant contains both male and female sex cells. The plants can self-fertilise and produce seeds. Mendel cross-fertilised the plants by taking pollen from one plant and brushing it onto the female parts of another plant.

At first Mendel investigated the shape of the seeds. He crossed round-seed plants with wrinkled-seed plants. All of the first (F1) generation produced round seeds.

a What does this tell you about the allele for round seed?

Mendel then crossed two round-seed plants from the F1 generation. He planted the seeds and grew the F2 generation of plants. He got 5474 round-seed plants and 1880 wrinkled-seed plants.

b i What is the ratio of round-seed plants to wrinkled-seed plants?
  ii Explain Mendel's results. Use a Punnett square to support your explanation.

c Mendel also worked with tall and dwarf plants. Here are his results:

F1: all tall;

F2: 787 tall, 277 dwarf.

  i Choose suitable symbols and write down the dominant and recessive genotypes and phenotypes.
  ii Use a Punnett square to explain Mendel's results for the F2 generation of tall and dwarf pea plants.

10.9 Evolution

Key points

- Evolution occurs as a result of the variation produced by sexual reproduction.
- Natural selection ensures that those individuals that best suit their environment are the ones that survive.
- Evolution occurs when the environment changes.
- Fossils provide us with a record of past evolution.

1 Copy the following table but match each key word with its correct meaning.

key word	meaning
evolution	failure of organisms to adapt to changes in the environment
fossil	differences that exist between organisms
variation	adaptation of organisms to changes in the environment through natural selection
extinction	the preserved remains of a dead organism

2 Charles Darwin sailed the Pacific Ocean and visited the Galapagos Islands. The islands are hundreds of miles from the coast of South America. The diagram shows three types of finch that lived on one of the islands.

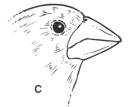

a Match each of the finches A–C to its description.
  i Feeds on large insects and large seeds;
  ii Feeds by picking small insects off leaves and twigs;
  iii Feeds on some small insects and soft seeds.

Darwin suggested that the three types of finch on the island had evolved from one type of finch which was found in South America.

b The finch in South America had a thick beak. Explain how the other finches with different beaks could have evolved.

3 When visiting a remote uninhabited island, scientists discovered colonies of geranium plants. The flowers were not the usual red or white but were bright blue. The scientists believed that these plants could have evolved as a result of natural selection in action on a mutant blue-flowering geranium.

a Explain how this genetic mutation could have arisen.

b Explain how natural selection could have produced these colonies of blue-flowering geraniums.

4 Use the information below to draw a time line. The information is not in the correct order.

- Dinosaurs became extinct about 60 million years ago.
- The first life was in water.
- Dinosaurs lived from 200 million years to 65 million years ago.
- Life moved onto land about 300 million years ago.
- The first of our ape-like ancestors lived 6 million years ago.
- Fish were the first vertebrates to appear – 400 million years ago.
- The first mammals that looked like shrews or mice started to appear about 65 million years ago.
- Reptiles started to evolve from amphibians about 200 million years ago.

IDEAS AND EVIDENCE

5 Explain why early scientists regarded the work of Mendel as proof of how characteristics are inherited, whereas the work of Darwin was regarded as evidence but not proof for evolution.

6 Charles Darwin formed his ideas on evolution only about 150 years ago. His famous voyage of discovery on *The Beagle* began in 1831 and his book *On the Origin of Species* was published in 1859. Imagine you are the science editor for a newspaper in 1859. Write the news headlines introducing Darwin's controversial book.

A1.1 **A balanced diet**

Key points

- To function correctly the body needs substances from the seven different types of food molecules.

- The need for many of these substances can be demonstrated by studying deficiency diseases.
- Other diseases can be caused by the intake of too much of a certain food substance.

1

a i What is a balanced diet?

ii List the seven different types of food molecules that are needed as part of a balanced diet.

b The information in the table below is taken from the label on a tin of baked beans.

	amount per 100 g	amount per serving (207 g)
energy in kJ/kcal	312/75	646/155
protein in g	4.7	9.7
carbohydrate in g (of which sugars)	13.6 (6.0)	28.2 (12.4)
fat in g (of which saturates)	0.2 (trace)	0.4 (0.1)
fibre in g	3.7	7.7
sodium in g	0.5	1.0

i Each 100 g of baked beans supplies 312 kJ of energy. Which types of food molecules would the energy be released from?

ii Which types of food molecules are not included on the label?

iii What does the body use protein for?

iv There is 3.7 g of fibre in 100 g baked beans. Why does the body need fibre?

v Suggest one reason (not already discussed) why eating baked beans would be part of a healthy diet.

2 The diagram below shows a section through a tooth with some decay.

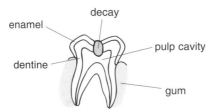

a Explain how the tooth decay has been caused. Include the following words in your explanation:
- **bacteria** • **food/glucose** • **acids**

b Prepare a discussion document showing arguments for and against eating between meals.

c List at least four ways in which you can try to prevent tooth decay.

3

a Keep an accurate diary of what you eat each day for a week.

b At the end of each day work out which types of food molecules you have eaten and which type you have not eaten. Look at the food labels if you are not sure. An example is shown below.

day	food	contains
Monday	cereal, milk, fruit juice	carbohydrates, calcium, protein, vitamins, minerals

4 Below is a table listing substances needed by the body, examples of foods that are rich in the substance and the deficiency disease that results from its lack.

substance	food rich in	deficiency disease
		kwaskiorkor
calcium		
		anaemia
	carrots	
	citrus fruits	
vitamin D		

a Copy and complete the table.

b Too much fat in the diet can lead to blockage of the arteries in the heart.
   i Name the arteries affected.
   ii Name the disease.

c Sailors a long time ago used to suffer from scurvy. Explain why.

d List the problems a person might have if there is too much sugar in their diet.

A1.2 Diets and requirements

Key points

- A person needs different amounts of the various food molecules at different times in their life.

- Sometimes people change their food intake by putting themselves on a particular diet.

1 The table below shows the amount of protein needed per day by different people.

person	protein needed in g per day
child aged 2 years	40
girl aged 5 years	50
girl aged 12 years	80
boy aged 12 years	60
boy aged 15 years	100
pregnant woman	90
nursing mother	100
man aged 35 years, resting	60

a Draw a bar chart of the data in the table.

b Comment on the overall pattern shown by these results in terms of:
  i age;
  ii gender.

c Suggest why there is a difference between the man resting and the 15-year-old boy.

d Explain why a woman needs a high intake of protein:
  i during pregnancy
  ii while breast-feeding the baby.

e The 12-year old girl needs 80 g protein per day. Suggest why this is more than the 5-year-old girl needs.

2 School meals are traditionally thought of as consisting of meat and two vegetables, followed by a stodgy pudding. More recently, schools have started serving snack-type meals such as chips, burgers and pizzas.

Prepare a leaflet for school students showing the advantages and disadvantages of each type of meal. Include problems caused by eating each type of school meal regularly.

3 The following chart gives information about body mass. Doctors and nutritionists use a chart like this to check if an individual is the correct weight.

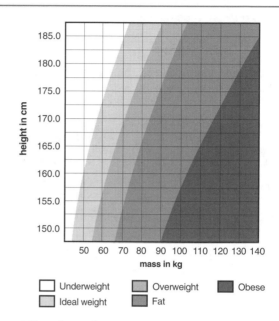

Underweight · Ideal weight · Overweight · Fat · Obese

a What does obese mean?

b John is 175 cm tall and has a mass of 90 kg. He likes playing computer games.
  i Which weight category does he fit into?
  ii Suggest three ways in which he could reduce his mass.
  iii What health problems might he have because of his mass?

c Jane is 185 cm tall and has a mass of 50 kg.
  i Which weight category does she fit into?
  ii Suggest three ways in which she could increase her mass.
  iii What health problems might she have because of her mass?

4

a i Describe the symptoms of anorexia.
  ii Suggest reasons for an increase in the condition in the last few years.

b i What is vegetarianism?
  ii Why does a vegetarian need to be careful about their diet?

c i How is a vegan different to a vegetarian?
  ii Explain why vegans need to take vitamin B12 supplements.
  iii Explain why vegans need extra plant protein.

A1.3 Physiology of exercise

Key points

- The heart rate is adjusted in order to keep the blood pressure as constant as possible.
- During exercise, the heart rate and breathing rate increase in order to meet the extra demands of the muscles.
- These changes are brought about by nerves and hormones.

1 The table below shows the effect of exercise on breathing rate and depth.

	rate in breaths per min	depth in cm^3 per breath
at rest	15	500
after exercise	40	1000

a i Calculate the total volume of air inhaled in 1 minute while at rest.
 ii Calculate the total volume of air inhaled in 1 minute after exercise.
 iii Explain the difference between the two values in parts i and ii.

b Inhaled air is 20% oxygen. Exhaled air is 16% oxygen. Calculate the volume of oxygen that diffuses into the blood in 1 minute.

c Explain why more oxygen needs to be absorbed into the blood during exercise than at rest.

d Explain how the body brings about the increase in rate and depth of breathing.

2 Blood pressure can be monitored constantly. The trace below shows such a recording.

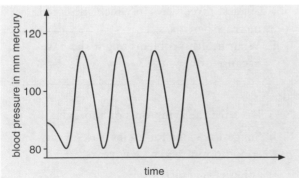

Blood pressure measurements have two components: systolic and diastolic.

a i What is systole?
 ii What is diastole?
 iii If blood pressure is '120 over 80', what does this mean?

b Copy the blood pressure trace and on it mark:
 i an X where systole is occurring;
 ii a Y where diastole is occurring.

c Why does the pressure fluctuate?

d Suggest what might increase the frequency of fluctuation.

e Changes in blood pressure can be dangerous. Describe what could happen if a person had:
 i high blood pressure;
 ii low blood pressure.

3 Adrenaline is sometimes called the 'fight or flight' hormone because it prepares the body for exertion and heightens the response to stimuli.

a i Name the gland that releases adrenaline.
 ii Describe its position in the body.

b Adrenaline acts on several parts of the body and has many effects. Explain each of the following statements.

 i Adrenaline diverts the blood from the digestive and reproductive systems to the muscles, lungs and liver.
 ii Adrenaline dilates the pupils of the eye.
 iii Adrenaline dilates the bronchioles in the lungs.
 iv Glycogen in the liver is converted to glucose.
 v Adrenaline inhibits peristalsis.
 vi Adrenaline causes cells to metabolise glucose more rapidly.
 vii In animals, adrenaline causes hair to stand on end.

IDEAS AND EVIDENCE

4 Exercise is good for the body as long as it does not strain the muscles, bones and joints beyond their limits. Overuse can result in injury. The body can adjust to physical demands made upon it by training.

Write about the injuries that can be sustained during exercise and how training can prevent them happening.

A1.4 Excretion

Key points

H The kidney contains millions of units called nephrons.

H Each nephron consists of a blood supply and a long tubule that filters the blood and

then reabsorbs certain substances according to the body's needs.

H People whose kidneys fail to work properly may have to use a kidney dialysis machine.

---

1 The diagram below shows a section through a kidney.

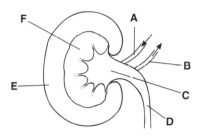

a Copy the diagram and complete labels A–F.

b Make a table to show the differences between the blood in vessels A and B.

---

2 The diagram below shows the detail of a nephron.

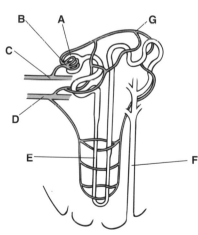

a Copy the diagram and complete labels A–G.

b Make a table to summarise the parts of the nephron and the functions of each.

3

a Explain the meaning of the following terms:
  i excretion;
  ii osmoregulation.

b Why is the kidney an organ of:
  i excretion;
  ii osmoregulation?

---

4 The diagram below shows the detail of a dialysis machine.

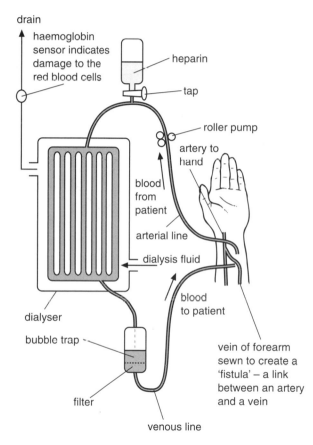

a What type of membrane is used in the dialyser?

b Why is a bubble trap included?

c Explain why heparin is added.

d The blood flow is in the opposite direction to the dialysing fluid. Explain why.

e Why is there no protein in the urine or the filtrate?

---

5 Describe and explain the effect the following would have on the composition and amount of urine:

a running a marathon;

b drinking 10 pints of lager;

c swimming for 30 minutes;

d eating a packet of salted peanuts.

A1.5 The brain and responses

- Sensory neurones enter the spinal cord through the dorsal root of the spinal nerves; motor neurones leave through the ventral root.
- Some responses are reflexes, which may or may not involve the brain.

- The brain has different regions which are responsible for different functions.
- The muscles are the main effectors in the body.

---

1 The diagram below shows a section through the head.

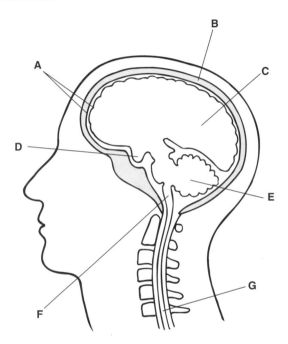

a Copy the diagram and complete labels A–G.

b The table below lists parts of the head. Copy the table and complete the right-hand column with the function(s) of the parts.

part	function(s)
cranium	
meninges	
cerebellum	
cerebrum	1 2 3
medulla oblongata	1 2

c List three ways in which scientists can find out about brain function.

---

2 The table below is about reflexes.

name	receptor	stimulus	effector	response
pupil	rods and cones	light	iris muscle	change in pupil size
knee jerk				
swallowing				
coughing				
sneezing				
blinking				

a i Copy and complete the table, using the example to guide you.
 ii Add any other reflexes you know.

b All reflexes have the same characteristics. State three of these characteristics.

c Describe an investigation you could do to show the pupillary reflex. Include results and an explanation of your results.

---

3 Smudge is a 10-year-old cat. When he was a kitten, Smudge's owner rattled his food dish as she called Smudge in for his supper each evening. Now Smudge comes when his dish is rattled, without being called.

a What is this type of behaviour called?

b Explain your answer to i.

c Who first described this type of behaviour?

d This behaviour is a form of learning. It can be speeded up by rewards or punishment. Describe how Smudge could be taught to urinate outside rather than in the house.

A2.1 Classification

Key points

- Artificial classification systems are based on single characteristics.
- Modern classification systems are natural systems and often provide information about evolutionary pathways.

- The first step in classifying an organism is to place it into a kingdom, of which there are five.
- Organisms are named using the binomial system that was introduced by Carl Linnaeus.

1 Modern classification systems have five kingdoms.

a i Name the five kingdoms.
  ii Give an example of an organism belonging to each kingdom.
b i Classification is hierarchical. What does this mean?
  ii The diagram below shows the classification of the cat family. Which contains the larger number of individuals, phylum or class?

kingdom	animalia			
phylum	chordata			
class	mammalia			
order	carnivora			
family	*Felidae*			
genus	*panthera*		*felis*	
species	P. leo (lion)	P. tigris (tiger)	F. lynx (lynx)	F. sylvestris (wild cat)

c The genus and species names are given in Latin. What name is given to this two-word Latin naming system?
d Find out the Latin name for the following:
  i human;
  ii horse;
  iii dog.
e Find out the common names for the following:
  i *Helix aspersa*;
  ii *Musca domestica*;
  iii *Cancer pagurus*.
f i Name the classification level where the first letter of the name is an upper-case letter.
  ii Which part of the classification always begins with a lower-case letter?

2 Design and produce a poster to show the five kingdoms. Include pictures, diagrams, drawings and any relevant information about each of the kingdoms.

3 Two species of thrush, *Turdus merula* (blackbird) and *Turdus philomelos* (song thrush), are commonly found in our gardens.

a What is meant by the term species?
b Copy and complete the table to show the classification of these two birds.

common name	blackbird	song thrush
kingdom		
	chordata	
	aves	
genus		
species		

4 Copy and complete the grid.

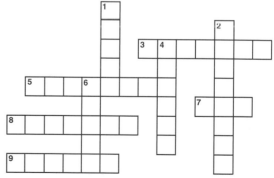

Across
3 Organisms that breed successfully together
5 Classifying organisms
7 A famous taxonomist
8 Plants, animals, fungi are this
9 This is the plural of the first part of the two-word Latin name

Down
1 Language of classification
2 Name of a famous person involved with classification
4 The second highest level in the hierarchy of classification
6 The fourth highest level in the hierarchy of classification

A2.2 Diversity and adaptation in plants

Key points

- The modern classification system that is usually used today has five kingdoms, one of which is plants.

- The most advanced phylum of plants is the flowering plants; they are well adapted to living on dry land.

1 Organisms are divided into five kingdoms. Plants and animals are two of these kingdoms. In spread 1.1 of the student course book you learnt about the structural differences between animal and plant cells. There are other differences between plants and animals: plants are autotrophic, whereas animals are heterotrophic.

a i What does autotrophic mean?

   ii Using examples, explain what heterotrophic means.

b Animals and plants differ in their response to stimuli. Describe the difference.

c Explain how the movements of plants and animals differ.

2 Flowering plants have become adapted to live in all areas of the world. Below are two lists, one of flowering plants and one of their habitats, but in the incorrect order. Copy the list of flowering plants and write the correct habitat beside each one.

flowering plants	habitats
cactus	wood
marram grass	moorland
sycamore	desert
reeds and rushes	mountains
heather	saltmarsh
edelweiss	fresh water
sea lavender	sand dunes

3 Bryophytes are one group of plants.

a List five plants included in this group.

b Name:
   i a fern;
   ii a conifer;
   iii a flowering plant.

c Name the group to which each of the following belongs:
   i buttercup;
   ii Christmas tree;
   iii mother-in-law's tongue.

d The table below shows the four main phyla of plants and features that identify them. Copy and complete the table by filling in the remaining phyla and the missing features.

phylum	features
bryophytes	1
	1 gametes need water 2
conifers	1 2
	1 enclosed gametes 2

4 Below is a list of ways in which a flowering plant is adapted to either insect or wind pollination. Create a table with two columns headed 'wind pollination' and 'insect pollination', and put each of the features into the correct column.

- large petals
- small petals
- colourful petals
- green petals
- scented
- no nectaries
- anthers outside flower
- stigma outside flower
- sticky pollen
- light pollen
- feathery stigma
- loose anthers

— IDEAS AND EVIDENCE —

5 The Saguaro cactus has the following features: no leaves, a thick green stem, thick waxy cuticle and dense spines.

a How do these features allow the Saguaro cactus to survive in the desert?

The desert has wide temperature variations. At night the air cools rapidly so that moisture in the air condenses and forms dew on the surface of the sand. The Echinocactus has a root system that extends a long way horizontally but does not go down very deep.

b Explain how the features of the Echinocactus's root system are useful adaptations for a plant living in the desert.

A2.3 Diversity and adaptation in animals

> ## Key points
>
> - Most habitats on earth have been colonised by animals, and these animals have become adapted to the conditions found in these habitats.
>
> - These adaptations include differences in the structure of their bodies, their body processes and their life cycles.

1 The camel is adapted to living in deserts. These deserts are hot dry places which provide little food. Some of the camel's adaptations are shown on the diagram below.

fat store in hump

large surface area   large feet

a **i** Copy and complete the table below to show how the adaptations of the camel help it to survive.

adaptation	how it helps the camel survive
fat stored in hump	
large surface area	
large feet	

   ii List other adaptations and explain your reasons for including them.

b Some animals are good predators. They are adapted for this in many ways. State features that a predator would need.

c The objects of predators are its prey. How are prey adapted to avoid being caught by the predator?

2 Construct a poster for your classroom wall showing the classification of the animal kingdom. Include pictures and diagrams of animals belonging to each group.

3 This is a list of features of a fish:

- gills • scales • operculum
- streamline shape • tail fin

Explain how each feature is an adaptation which enables the fish to live in water.

a Plaice and other flat fish have both eyes on the same side. Explain why.

b Some fish live in very deep water.
   i Suggest some features that these fish would need to survive.
   ii These fish are often blind. Why?

4 The diagram below represents a woodland area.

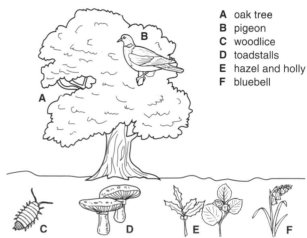

A oak tree
B pigeon
C woodlice
D toadstalls
E hazel and holly
F bluebell

Different organisms are found in different habitats in the wood. For each organism A–F, explain why it is found in that habitat.

5 The graph below shows the light outside and in the wood.

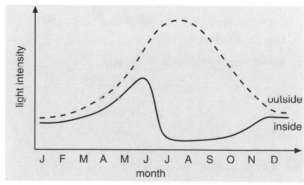

a Why does the light intensity in the wood fall in May?

b Why does the light intensity increase in October?

c Why is the light intensity reached in the wood in the autumn lower than the level in April and early May?

A3.1 Food poisoning

Key points

- Micro-organisms can cause food to go bad, which can lead to food poisoning.

- Hygienic practices can prevent food poisoning.
- Food can be preserved in a variety of ways.

1 The diagram below shows four thermometers in different places.

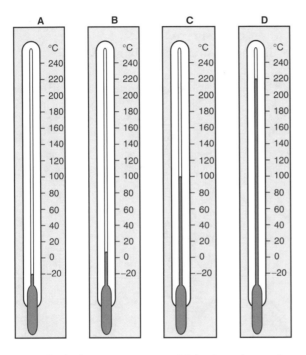

a i Which thermometer would be in a freezer?
ii Which would be in a fridge?
iii Which would be involved in making jam?
iv Which would be used in canning?

b The two lists below show ways of preserving food and foods that can be preserved. Copy the list of preservation methods and write the correct food alongside each.

preservation methods	foods
salting	ice cream
freezing	raisins
drying	shallots
pickling	cured ham

2 On returning home after a week away, Jo found that the bread she had left in the cupboard was covered in a green furry substance. The crisps and pickled onions she had forgotten to put away were as she had left them.

a i What is the green furry substance on the bread?

ii Explain why the bread had changed but the other foods had remained the same.

b Name five foods that are likely to go bad in a few days if not refrigerated.

3 Design a poster for a hotel kitchen to show good and bad food hygiene practices.

4 Some methods of food preservation involve osmosis.

a What is osmosis?

b Which of the following methods of preservation involve osmosis?

- canning • freezing • irradiating • pasteurising
- salting • using sugar • ultraheat treatment

c Explain how osmosis is used to preserve food.

5 Louis Pasteur discovered that there are microbes in the air which make food go bad. The diagrams below show the stages of an experiment that he did to show this.

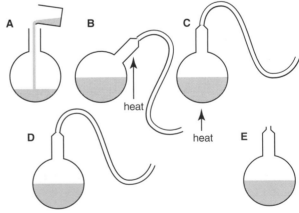

a What is being poured into the flask in A?

b Why is the neck of the flask heated in B?

c Why is the flask boiled again in C?

d What would you expect to see in D after several weeks? Explain your answer.

e The neck of the flask was then broken off. Explain how this would affect the results.

A3.2 Making food

Key points

- Micro-organisms are involved in the production of many foods.
- Micro-organisms can themselves be used as a food source.

1 The flow diagram below shows how cheese is made.

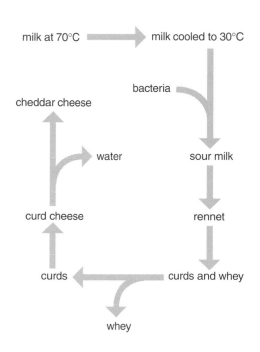

a Name the two types of cheese made.

b Why are bacteria added to the milk?

c Why is the milk cooled before the bacteria are added?

d Name two things that are added to the milk.

e Name two by-products.

f Suggest a use for whey.

g Why is the milk heated to 70°C at the beginning of the process?

2 The following recipe is for making bread.

Ingredients

flour
sugar
yeast
water
salt

Method

1. Mix the yeast with a little warm water, and leave for a few minutes.
2. Mix the flour and salt.
3. Add the yeast mixture to the flour mixture and stir until mixed together.
4. Leave the dough to prove for 30 minutes.
5. Place dough in a hot oven to cook for 10 minutes.

a   i What is yeast?
   ii Why is it used to make bread?
   iii What is the function of the sugar?

b   Why is the yeast mixed with warm rather than hot water?

c   Explain what happens when the dough is left to prove.

d   Anaerobic respiration is taking place.

  i State the word and chemical equations for the process.
  ii What happens to the products of respiration when the bread is placed in the hot oven?

3 Humans have used micro-organisms to make food for thousands of years. Yeasts, moulds and bacteria can be used. Copy and complete the table to show which of the three types of organism are used in making the foods listed.

food	organisms
wine	
cheese	
yoghurt	
vinegar	
beer	
bread	

4 People tend to be wary about new technology. A supermarket wants to educate its customers about single-cell protein (SCP). Prepare a leaflet about SCP, aimed at the general public. Explain what SCP is, how it is produced, how it is used, and why we do not need to be wary of it.

A3.3 Enzymes

Key points

H Micro-organisms use enzymes.
H Enzymes are sensitive to temperature and pH.

H Enzymes are substrate specific.
H A lock-and-key model can be used to explain how enzymes work.

1 The graph below shows the effect of temperature on enzyme activity in humans.

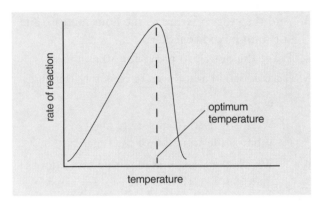

a i Explain what optimum means.
   ii What would you expect the optimum temperature to be for enzyme activity in humans?
b Describe the shape of the graph as the temperature rises.
c Explain your answer to **b**.
d Describe and explain the shape of the graph after the optimum temperature is reached.
e What conclusions can be reached from these data?
f What is an enzyme?
g Why are enzymes important in humans?

2 Design an investigation to find out the effect of pH during the digestion of protein by protease. Include details of apparatus, method, fair test, hypothesis, results, patterns, conclusions, and evaluation.

3 In an experiment to investigate the digestion of starch, solutions were tested for glucose and starch.

a i Describe how you would test for glucose and what results you would expect for both positive and negative outcomes.
   ii Describe how you would test for starch and what results you would expect for both positive and negative outcomes.

The table below shows the tests and the outcomes. A tick means present and a cross means absent.

test contents of tube	beginning		end	
	glucose	starch	glucose	starch
saliva and starch	✗	✓	✓	✗
boiled saliva and starch	✗	✓	✗	✓

b Why was saliva used?
c Explain why the end result for saliva and starch gave a positive glucose test.
d Where had the starch gone?
e Why was there no change in the tube containing boiled saliva?

4 Imagine you are a starch molecule in a slice of bread. Describe your journey through the human digestive system. Make particular reference to the parts of the digestive system you pass through, the enzymes that you meet, and the conditions in terms of temperature and pH. You can present your work as prose or as a poster.

5 In an experiment to show the effect of pH on enzyme activity, a starch–agar plate was set up with six holes cut in it, as shown in the diagram. Each hole contained the same amount and concentration of amylase but the pH of each was different. The numbers show the pH. The plate was left for 48 hours and then flooded with iodine.

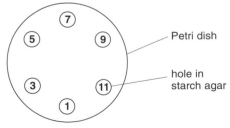

Draw the appearance of the starch–agar plate and give a detailed explanation of the results. (Hint: starch–agar goes clear when the starch has been digested.)

A3.4 **DNA makes protein**

> ### Key points
>
> H Each gene on the DNA codes for a specific protein.
> H DNA makes a template of the gene as RNA.
> H RNA constructs the protein from amino acids.
>
> H DNA from different sources can be recombined by genetic engineering. This is called recombinant DNA.

1

a i What is a gene?
   ii What does a gene do?
   iii Describe where in a cell genes are found.

b i DNA is an abbreviation. What is the full name?
   ii DNA is a double helix. What does this mean?

2 Design a poster to display in the laboratory showing how DNA from different sources can be recombined by genetic engineering. Your poster should include information on the enzymes used in genetic engineering.

3 The following statements explain how information in the nucleus codes for the manufacture of protein but they are given in the wrong order. Copy out the statements in the correct order.

- Chromosomes are made of DNA.
- The protein, for example haemoglobin, is made.
- The nucleus contains genetic information.
- Twenty different amino acids are used to build thousands of different proteins.
- DNA provides the instructions for how the cell works.
- Proteins are amino acids put together.
- Cells make proteins.
- The information is on chromosomes.
- A gene is a length of DNA.
- Each gene codes for the sequence of amino acids in a protein.

4 DNA when unwound is like a ladder. The two sides are joined by bases. This is shown in the following diagram.

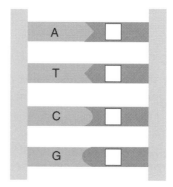

a i Copy the diagram and fill in the boxes to show the missing bases.
   ii Explain your choice of bases.

b Copy and complete the table below to show what A, T, C and G stand for.

initial	name of base
A	
T	
C	
G	

c The four bases code for more than 20 amino acids. Use the format below to write out all the possible combinations of two bases.

	T	C	G	A
T				
C				
G				
A				

d i How many possible combinations of two bases are there?
   ii Why is this not enough for the code?

e i Suggest how many bases are needed to code for one amino acid.
   ii Draw a table similar to the one above to show the possible combinations. How many are there?

A3.5 Biotechnology and food

1

a What is genetically modified food?

b Research and prepare a discussion document on the arguments for and against genetically modified food.

2 Cheese is made from milk. The table below shows the proportions of different food substances found in the milk from three different animals.

substance	percentage of substance in milk		
	cow	goat	sheep
fat	3.8	6.0	9.0
protein	3.0	3.3	4.6
minerals	0.8	0.8	1.0
sugar	4.8	4.6	4.7
water	87.6	85.3	80.7

a Display the data in the table as a bar chart.

b If 100 g of cows' milk makes 51.4 g of cheese, calculate the amount of cheese that could be made from 100 g of goats' milk.

3 Chymosin (rennin) is an enzyme used in cheese making. It is produced by mammals. It can now be produced by micro-organisms that have been genetically engineered.

a Describe how micro-organisms can be changed genetically so that they produce chymosin.

b Cheese produced in this way could be labelled as being made using genetically engineered organisms.

  i Suggest why labelling genetically modified foods may increase their sales.

  ii Suggest why labelling genetically modified foods may decrease their sales.

4 Enzymes are important in biotechnology as industrial catalysts.

a What is a catalyst?

b List the properties of enzymes that must be considered when they are used.

c Enzymes can be made by micro-organisms in a fermenter. A batch fermenter is shown in the following diagram.

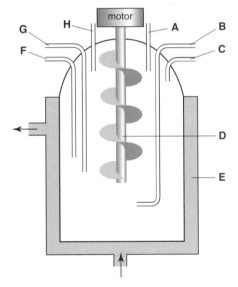

  i Copy the diagram and add annotations to explain the function of each part of the fermenter labelled A–H.

  ii What is meant by the term batch fermenter?

  iii Explain how batch fermentation differs from continuous fermentation.

IDEAS AND EVIDENCE

5 Biotechnology is not a new concept. Man has been using biotechnology for thousands of years. It is used in the brewing industry to make wine, beer and spirits, and in the baking industry. It is also important in the manufacture of cheese, yoghurt and vinegar.

Design a poster to show how biotechnology is used in the production of food by humans.

A4.1 Types of disease

Key points

- Non-infectious diseases can be caused by our genes or by the environment.
- Infectious diseases are caused by micro-organisms.
- Bacteria, fungi and viruses are examples of micro-organisms that cause disease.

1 Infectious diseases can be caused by micro-organisms. The diagrams below show four types of micro-organism.

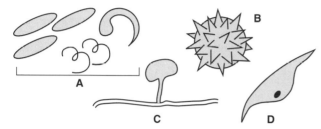

a Name each type of disease-causing organism A–D.

b The following is a list of features of bacteria and viruses. Make a table to show which are features of bacteria and which are features of viruses.

- Reproduce quickly
- Coat made of protein
- Size about $\frac{1}{10\,000}$ mm
- Size about $\frac{1}{100\,000}$ mm
- Can produce poisons
- Has a cell wall
- Slime capsule present
- Always contains DNA
- Contains cytoplasm

2 Copy the table below and fill in the type of micro-organism that causes each disease.

disease	type of micro-organism
influenza	
athlete's foot	
sore throat	
sleeping sickness	
tetanus	
polio	
malaria	
ringworm	
food poisoning	

3 Make a poster showing:

a how viruses are spread;

b examples of the main types of bacteria.

4

a Explain the difference between infectious and non-infectious diseases.

b Non-infectious diseases fall into several categories. List the categories and give an example of each. For example, nicotine addiction is a self-inflicted disease.

5 Draw an outline of the body (at least A4 size). Use annotated labels to show how micro-organisms can enter the body. You might prefer to do this poster size for display.

6 Imagine you are a common-cold virus. Write a story about your adventures over the last 100 years.

7 Copy and complete the following table to show how the diseases are spread.

disease	how spread
tetanus	
cold/flu	
cholera	
sleeping sickness	
plague	
sexually transmitted disease	
diphtheria	
athlete's foot	

A4.2 HIV, AIDS and parasites

Key points

- Human immunodeficiency virus (HIV) infects the white blood cells.
- AIDS is the ultimate effect of HIV infection.
- Parasites can be spread from person to person.

1

a What is a parasite?

b Parasites can live in or on an organism.

  i What adaptations might a parasite need to live on an organism?

  ii Imagine you are a tapeworm living in the small intestine. Explain what adaptations you might need and what difficulties you might face.

c The diagram below shows the human body and some of its parasites. Find out and write about each of the parasites shown in the diagram.

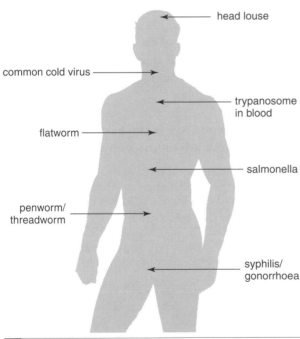

- head louse
- common cold virus
- trypanosome in blood
- flatworm
- salmonella
- penworm/threadworm
- syphilis/gonorrhoea

2 Make a poster about the different types of worms that can live in the human body.

3 It is often stated that AIDS is a homosexual disease. Explain in detail why this statement is not accurate.

4 Disease can be caused by parasites. There are ways of stopping the spread of these diseases. Here is a list of organisms that cause disease.

- athlete's foot • tapeworm • malarial parasite
- head lice • toxocara worm

a Copy and complete the table below by writing in the correct organism from the list.

way of stopping spread	organism
do not come into contact with animal faeces	
avoid head-to-head contact	
use mosquito nets	
check meat before selling	
do not walk barefoot in wet places	

b The diagram below shows a head louse.

  i How are head lice adapted to live on hair?

  ii How do the eggs stay on the head/hair?

5 Since its first appearance in California in 1981, no disease has received so much public attention. The cause was identified in 1983, and in 1986 it was named HIV.

a What does HIV stand for?

b Explain the difference between HIV and AIDS.

c List the ways in which HIV can be spread.

d State five ways in which the spread of HIV can be prevented and controlled.

e To combat AIDS, social and medical responses are needed. Prepare an argument for and against the statement 'all people should have a blood test to see if they carry HIV'.

A4.3 Antiseptics and antibiotics

Key points

- Antiseptics are chemicals that kill micro-organisms. They are used externally on the skin.

- Antibiotics are drugs that kill bacteria. They can be taken internally.

1

a How is an antiseptic different from an antibiotic?

b What is the difference between an antiseptic and a disinfectant?

c What is the difference between penicillin and *Penicillium*?

d Who discovered penicillin?

e Whose work led to the manufacture of penicillin on a commercial scale?

f Some people are allergic to penicillin.

   i What symptoms would they have?

   ii What does allergic mean?

2 Sam went to the doctor because she had a cold. The doctor would not give Sam any antibiotics and told her to go home, keep warm and drink plenty of fluids. Explain why the doctor took this action.

 3 In an investigation into illness, mice were infected with the same type and amount of bacteria. They were then given penicillin at different times of the day. Their survival rates are shown in the table below.

mouse	dose of penicillin in mg						survival time in days
	11 a.m.	1 p.m.	3 p.m.	5 p.m.	7 p.m.	9 p.m.	
A	10	0	0	0	0	0	4
B	5	5	5	5	5	0	recovered

a Suggest why mouse B recovered.

b Why must you complete a course of antibiotics even if you feel better?

c Some antibiotics kill bacteria whereas others prevent the bacteria from dividing. Bacteria were grown in three tubes. Equivalent doses of different antibiotics were added to each tube. The number of living bacteria was counted every hour for 10 hours. The following graph shows the results.

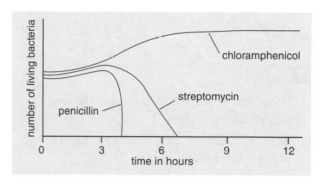

i Which antibiotic killed the bacteria fastest?

ii Explain your answer to i.

iii Which antibiotic had little, if any, effect on the number of bacteria?

iv Explain your answer to iii.

v Why are antibiotics useful even if they only stop bacteria dividing?

4

a Describe an investigation to show how different antibiotics affect the growth of bacteria. Include diagrams, detail of apparatus, method, safety precautions etc.

b The diagram below shows the results of such an investigation.

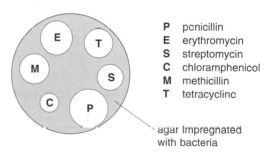

P penicillin
E erythromycin
S streptomycin
C chloramphenicol
M methicillin
T tetracycline

agar impregnated with bacteria

i How can you tell which antibiotics were effective?

ii List the antibiotics in order, most effective first.

iii Explain how you decided which antibiotic was most effective.

5 Prepare a document discussing the arguments for and against the use of animals in testing antibiotics.

A4.4 Immunisation

Key points

- The basis of immunisation is injecting dead or a mild form of the pathogen, against which the body makes antibodies.
- Some viruses such as the common cold can change their structure so that a vaccine is no longer effective.
- Edward Jenner produced the first vaccine against smallpox.
- Pathogens can be used to control pests.

1

a Name the scientist who produced the first vaccine against rabies.

b Name the scientist who produced the first vaccine against smallpox.

c How does a vaccine protect against a specific disease?

d The development of a vaccine against rabies includes the following steps. The steps have been set out in the wrong order. Copy out the steps in the correct order.

- The spinal cord is taken out of the dead rabbit and dried to weaken the virus.
- The weakened virus is injected into a person.
- The rabies virus is extracted from the infected dog.
- The weakened virus is injected into a living rabbit.

e Why is it important to vaccinate someone before they get a disease rather than afterwards?

2

a List in a chart all the vaccinations you have had and the dates when you received them.

b Construct a second table to show possible vaccinations and when you should receive them.

c Find out which vaccinations you should have when travelling abroad.

3 The vaccine against TB is called BCG. It is a live, weakened vaccine. It can be kept for 1 year at a low temperature. The vaccine is intended for 10–13 year olds. It provides protection for at least 10 years. Some people feel slightly unwell after receiving the vaccination.

a Suggest why some people feel unwell after receiving the BCG vaccination.

b State three precautions that should be taken when giving the injection.

c Some people are immune to TB. Explain how they obtained this immunity.

d Who developed the BCG vaccine?

e Before a BCG vaccination is given, a Mantoux test is done. Draw a series of diagrams to explain the Mantoux test, its possible results, and the outcomes in terms of whether the BCG vaccination is given.

4 The following graph shows the number of people in the UK who have had tuberculosis (TB) and the number of sufferers who have died from the disease.

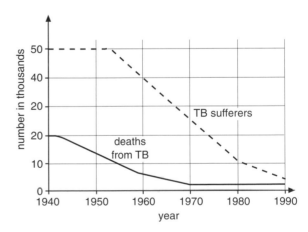

a Suggest which year vaccinations against TB began.

b From the graph determine:
   i   the number of sufferers in 1960;
   ii the number of deaths in 1960.
   iii Calculate the percentage of sufferers that died in 1960.

IDEAS AND EVIDENCE

5 Find out and write about how Edward Jenner demonstrated how vaccination works.

A4.5 **Plants and disease**

Key points

- Infectious diseases can affect plants

- The diseases can be controlled by selective breeding, chemical treatments and a variety of farming methods

---

1

a Name five plant diseases.

b Copy and complete the table below to show a plant disease caused by each type of organism.

organism	disease
bacteria	
viruses	
fungi	

2 Chemical treatments can be used to control infectious plant diseases. Write about one chemical method of control.

3

a What is potato blight?

b Name the organism that causes potato blight.

c List the symptoms of the disease.

d Describe how you might attempt to control the disease.

e Draw a series of sketches to show how the organism infects the potato and causes the disease.

4 One method of controlling plant diseases is by breeding. Agriculturalists have two types of potato plant: plant A is a heavy cropper but very susceptible to disease; plant B is very resistant to disease. They want to cross the plants in an attempt to produce a resistant heavy cropper.

They select the best examples of each type, wait for them to flower and then start the program:

Stage 1 – remove the stamens from plant B.
Stage 2 – transfer pollen from flower B to flower A.
Stage 3 – cover plant A with a polythene bag.

a Explain why each stage is needed.

b Explain in detail what the agriculturalist would do next in breeding these potatoes.

5 The table below shows a pattern of crop rotation.

field	year		
	1	**2**	**3**
A	cereal	carrots	
B		cereal	carrots
C		beans	

a Copy and complete the table.

b Carrots are deep rooted. Why is this an advantage in a crop rotation system?

c Cereals are shallow rooted. Why is this an advantage in a crop rotation system?

d Explain why beans are included in the crop rotation system.

e How does this system prevent the survival of parasites and hence disease?

6 The following diagrams show how grafting is done.

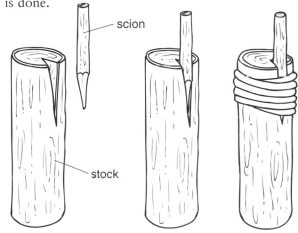

a What features would a gardener look for when choosing a stock?

b What features would a gardener look for when choosing a scion?

c Explain why a gardener might choose the grafting method of vegetative reproduction.

d Describe how grafting works.

Glossary (TB 1–10)

Terms set in *bold italic* are higher-tier material.

23 pairs (10.2) – the number of pairs of chromosomes found in a normal cell.

46 chromosomes (10.2) – the number of chromosomes found in a normal cell.

A

absorption (2.3) – movement of soluble food molecules from the digestive system into the bloodstream

acid rain (7.7) – rain that has a low pH due to dissolved sulphur dioxide and other impurities

active transport (1.3) – the movement of substances across a cell membrane using energy from respiration. This is usually against a concentration gradient. In some cases substances are transported down a diffusion gradient by active transport, speeding up movement that would be too slow by diffusion.

adaptation (7.2) – the characteristics of an organism that make it well suited to living in a particular environment.

ADH (9.3) – a hormone that regulates the water level in the body by increasing reabsorption in the renal tubules.

air movement (6.5) – the rate of transpiration increases as the speed of the air movement increases.

air spaces (5.1) – spaces within a leaf that allow air to move between the cells.

alcohol (3.2) – a substance produced by anaerobic respiration in yeast.

allele (10.7) – a genetic instruction received from one parent. Alleles from both parents form a gene.

alveoli (4.1) – small air sacs found in the lungs (singular = alveolus).

amylase (2.1) – an enzyme that digests starch to maltose.

anabolic steroids (8.5) – hormones that result in a build up of muscle tissue in the body.

anaerobic (3.2) – respiration without oxygen.

antibodies (6.3) – chemicals produced by the body's immune system to destroy foreign invading organisms.

aorta (6.2) – the main artery that carries blood from the heart, out to the body.

artery (6.1, 6.2) – blood vessel that carries blood away from the heart.

atrium (6.2) – the left and right atria are the two upper muscular chambers of the heart. They pump blood into the ventricles.

auxin (8.6) – a plant hormone that is produced in the growing points. It stimulates the growth of a shoot.

B

bases (10.1) – the four chemicals A, T, C and G that code for the instructions of life on DNA.

Benedict's solution (2.1) – a chemical reagent that is used to test for reducing sugars. It gives an orange colour when boiled with a reducing sugar.

bile (2.2) – a liquid produced in the liver and stored in the gall bladder. It is released into the small intestine and contains bile salts.

bile salts (2.2) – chemicals found in bile that emulsify fats.

biological control (7.6) – the use of a living organism to control a pest population.

Biuret test (2.1) – a chemical test used to detect proteins. Solutions of sodium hydroxide and copper sulphate are used, and give a purple colour with proteins.

blind spot (8.1) – the area of the retina where the optic nerve leaves. This area does not contain light-sensitive cells.

blood (9.1) – a red liquid that transports nutrients, oxygen and other materials around the body.

blood pressure (6.1) – a measure of the pressure of the blood when the heart is contracting and when it is relaxing.

blood vessels (9.2) – tubes that carry blood around the body and back to the heart.

brain (8.3) – the enlarged front end of the CNS, responsible for much of the co-ordination in the body.

breathing rate (4.2) – the number of cycles of inhalation and exhalation in one minute.

bronchi (4.1) – two tubes that lead from the trachea into the lungs (singular = bronchus).

bronchioles (4.1) – small tubes in the lungs that lead from the bronchi to the alveoli.

bronchitis (4.3) – a disease caused by fluid collecting in the alveoli and becoming infected.

C

calorimeter (3.1) – a device for measuring the energy content of food. The units of measurement used to be calories but are now joules.

capillary (6.1) – tiny blood vessel that carries blood to the tissues of the body. A human being has thousands of miles of capillaries.

carbon cycle (7.5) – a scheme that describes how the element carbon is recycled in nature.

carbon dioxide (5.2) – a gas produced by respiration, in both plants and animals.

cell membrane (1.1) – a thin structure, made of protein and fat, that surrounds every cell.

cellulose (5.3) – a substance made by plants that forms the structure of their cell walls.

cell wall (1.1) – a tough protective structure made of cellulose that surround the cell membrane in plant cells.

chlorophyll (5.1, 5.3) – a green pigment produced by plants that is used to trap light energy for the process of photosynthesis.

chloroplasts (1.1, 5.1) – plant cell organelles that contain chlorophyll and are the site of photosynthesis.

chromosomes (10.1) – structures composed of DNA and found in the nuclei of cells.

cilia (4.3) – small hair-like structures on the surface of cells. They beat in a co-ordinated way in order to move the cell or move external substances.

ciliary muscle (8.1) – a circular muscle that passes around the lens. It is composed of circular and longitudinal fibres and is used to change the shape of the lens. It is often referred to as the ciliary body.

clone (10.5) – two or more organisms that are genetically identical.

CNS (8.3) – the central nervous system, part of the nervous system, consisting of the brain and spinal cord.

community (7.1) – all the organisms that live in a particular habitat.

competition (7.2) – continual struggle that organisms have with each other for resources.

concentration gradient (1.3) – the variation in concentration of a substance in two different areas.

cones (8.1) – sensory cells in the retina of the eye that are sensitive to coloured light. Different cones are sensitive to different wavelengths.

conservation (7.8) – process of maintaining the environment in a natural state so that habitats and organisms can survive and flourish.

co-ordination (8.3) – process by which all the sensory information is monitored and responses initiated for the benefit of the organism as a whole.

cornea (8.1) – the transparent layer of tissue at the front of the eye that is responsible for most refraction of light in the eye.

cutting (8.7) – an artificial way of making genetically identical copies of plants by removing and planting sections of stems.

cystic fibrosis (10.4) – an inherited disease caused by a recessive allele. Only people with two recessive alleles have the disease. It causes thick mucous secretions to be produced, leading to lung damage and digestion problems.

cytoplasm (1.1) – contents of a cell outside the nucleus, made up mainly of water with dissolved chemicals, and organelles.

D

decomposers (7.5) – organisms that feed on dead organic remains by secreting enzymes onto them and taking up the semi-digested food.

decomposition (7.5) – breakdown of dead organic material by decomposers.

denitrifying (7.5) – process by which nitrates are broken down to release nitrogen gas.

depressant (8.2) – drug that reduces the activity of the nervous system.

diabetes (9.1) – a disease in which a person does not produce enough insulin to control the level of sugar in the blood.

dialysis (9.3) – a technique similar to osmosis, used in kidney machines to filter the blood of impurities.

diaphragm (4.1) – sheet of muscle that separates the thorax from the abdomen.

diffuse/diffusion (1.3, 6.1) – net passive movement of particles from an area of high concentration to an area of low concentration.

DNA (10.1, 10.6) – the molecule that codes for all the instructions needed to make an organism, and is also capable of replication.

dominant (10.7) – an allele that expresses itself in the phenotype.

Down's syndrome (10.4) – a genetic disease caused by having an extra chromosome 21.

ductless (8.4) – characteristic of hormone-producing glands which lack ducts but release their secretions straight into the bloodstream.

E

electron microscope (1.1) – a device that magnifies structures to high resolution by using a beam of electrons.

emphysema (4.3) – a disease caused by breakdown of the walls of alveoli, thus reducing gaseous exchange.

emulsification (2.2) – the process of breaking down fat droplets into smaller ones.

energy (3.1, 5.1) – the ability to do work.

energy flow (7.4) – the transfer of energy through an ecosystem.

engulf (6.3) – to swallow up.

enzymes (9.2) – organic catalysts that speed up the rate of a reaction.

epithelium (4.3) – the layer of cells that covers surfaces inside and outside the body (plural = epithelia).

evolution (10.9) – adaptation of organisms to changes in the environment through natural selection.

extinct(ion) (7.8, 10.9) – failure of organisms to adapt to changes in the environment so that they die out.

F1 generation (10.7) – the first generation produced from two true-breeding parents.

F2 generation (10.7) – the generation produced from crossing two F1 individuals.

fermentation (3.2) – anaerobic respiration in organisms such as yeast.

fertilise/fertilisation (10.5) – the fusion of male and female sex cells.

filtered (9.3) – performed by renal tubules to remove urea from the blood.

flaccid (1.4) – situation in plant cells that have lost water by osmosis so that the cytoplasm does not push against the cell wall.

fossil (10.9) – the preserved remains of a dead organism.

fovea (8.1) – area of the retina that contains the highest concentration of light-sensitive cells (cones).

gamete (10.5) – a cell involved in reproduction, such as an ovum or a sperm.

gastric juice (2.2) – the acidic liquid that is secreted by the glands lining the stomach. It contains protein-digesting enzymes.

gene (10.1, 10.6) – a section of DNA that codes for one specific instruction.

genetic cloning (10.6) – a technique used to produce genetically identical organisms.

genotype (10.7) – a description of the two alleles that form a gene.

geotropism (8.6) – a growth response in plants either towards or away from gravity.

glucose (3.1, 5.3, 9.1, 9.3) – a substance that is produced by photosynthesis and used as an energy source in respiration.

glycogen (9.1) – a substance stored in the liver and formed when excess glucose is present in the blood.

goblet cells (4.3) – cells lining the various tubes in the lungs which secrete mucus.

greenhouse effect (7.7) – the process by which various gases in the Earth's atmosphere trap heat, thereby keeping the atmosphere warm.

guard cells (6.4) – two cells that control the opening and closing of a stoma.

habitat (7.1) – an area where organisms live, with specific environmental conditions.

hepatic portal vein (2.3) – the vein that takes blood, rich in dissolved food, from the small intestine to the liver.

heterozygous (10.7) – a gene that consists of two different alleles.

homozygous (10.7) – a gene that consists of two identical alleles.

hormones (8.4, 9.1) – chemical messengers released from various glands which reach their target organ(s) via the blood.

host (7.3) – a live organism that is fed upon by a parasite.

humidity (6.5) – a measure of the amount of water vapour in the atmosphere.

ileum (2.3) – the last part of the small intestine that is the site for most absorption of food into the bloodstream.

infertility (8.5) – the inability to conceive.

inherited (10.3) – passed from parent to child via the genes.

insecticides (7.6) – chemicals that kill insects.

insulin (8.4, 9.1) – a hormone, produced by the pancreas, that reduces the level of glucose in the blood.

intensive (7.6) – a system of farming that uses modern technology to produce maximum possible yields.

intercostal muscles (4.1) – two sets of muscles that move the ribs, allowing breathing to occur.

iodine solution (2.1) – a chemical consisting of iodine dissolved in potassium iodide. It is used to test for starch, turning a blue–black colour on contact.

iris (8.1) – the coloured area around the pupil of the eye. It contains muscles that change the diameter of the pupil according to the light conditions.

joule (3.1) – a unit for measuring energy.

kidneys (9.3) – organs that control the water level of the body and removes urea from the blood.

kidney tubules (9.3) – structures in the kidney that filter the blood.

lacteals (2.3) – lymphatic vessels that are found in villi. They absorb some of the products of digestion, particularly fats.

lactic acid (3.2) – a chemical produced by anaerobic respiration in humans; it causes muscle fatigue.

law of independent assortment (10.8) – Mendel's law which states that any allele from a gene of one parent can combine with any allele of the same gene from the other parent.

law of segregation (10.8) – Mendel's law which states that the two alleles of a gene will go into different gametes at meiosis.

leaf (5.1) – the plant's 'green machine' that makes food by photosynthesis.

lens (8.1) – an elastic transparent structure in the eye that is responsible for the fine focusing of light.

light intensity (5.2) – one of the factors that can limit the rate of photosynthesis.

light microscope (1.1) – a device that uses light rays to produce a magnified image of an object.

limiting factor (5.2) – a factor that limits the rate of photosynthesis.

lipase (2.1) – an enzyme that digests fats to fatty acids and glycerol.

liver (9.1) – an organ of the body that stores glycogen and breaks down harmful toxins.

lung (6.2) – a respiratory surface found in mammals.

lung cancer (4.3) – a disease in which cells in the lungs divide in a rapid uncontrolled manner, forming a tumour.

M

magnesium (5.3) – a mineral salt required for the formation of chlorophyll.

meiosis (10.5) – cell division that occurs when gametes are produced; in humans it reduces the number of chromosomes from 46 to 23.

Mendel (10.8) – Augustinian monk who was called 'the father of genetics'.

menstrual cycle (8.5) – the recurring pattern of changes in a woman's reproductive organs. Each cycle usually lasts about 28 days.

menstruation (8.5) – the breakdown and loss of the inner lining of the uterus.

micropropagation (10.5) – a way of using individual cells to produce lots of identical plants.

microvilli (2.3) – microscopic projections found on the surface of the villi in the small intestine.

mineral salts (6.4) – essential minerals that are required by living organisms.

mitochondria (1.1) – microscopic organelles found in the cytoplasm of plant and animal cells. They are the site of many of the reactions of respiration (singular = mitochondrion).

mitosis (10.5) – cell division that produces identical copies of cells.

motor neurone (8.3) – a nerve cell that carries impulses from the CNS to the effectors.

mucus (4.3) – a slimy liquid that is secreted by goblet cells to provide lubrication and trap foreign particles.

mutation (10.3) – a change in the structure of a gene or DNA, caused by such things as chemicals, X-rays or radiation.

mutualism (7.3) – a relationship between two organisms of different species in which both organisms gain.

N

nastic (8.6) – a growth response by plants to a non-directional stimulus.

natural selection (10.9) – a process in which organisms that are most suited to the environment survive and produce more offspring.

nerve (8.2) – a collection of neurones held together in a bundle by connective tissue.

nerve impulse (8.2) – an electro-chemical change that passes along a neurone.

neurone (8.2) – a single nerve cell. Many neurones make up a nerve.

neurotransmitter (8.2) – a chemical that is released at a synapse when a nerve impulse arrives. It diffuses across the synapse and starts an impulse in the next nerve cell.

nitrifying (7.5) – the process that converts ammonium compounds to nitrates.

nitrogen (5.3) – a highly unreactive gas found in the air and required for protein production.

nitrogen fixing (7.5) – the process in which nitrogen gas is converted into nitrates and other compounds of nitrogen that can be used by plants.

nucleus (1.1, 10.1) – the area of a cell that contains the genetic material and so controls all the processes occurring in the cell.

O

oestrogen (8.5) – a hormone secreted by the ovaries which controls the female secondary sex characteristics.

optic nerve (8.1) – a collection of nerve cells that send information from the eyes to the brain.

optimum (9.2) – the optimum conditions are those at which the rate of reaction is fastest.

organ (1.2) – a structure made up of different tissues working together to perform a particular function.

osmoregulation (9.3) – control of the body's water level by the kidneys.

osmosis (1.4, 6.4) – the movement of water molecules from a dilute solution to a concentrated solution, through a partially permeable membrane.

ovum (10.5) – a female sex cell (plural = ova).

oxygen debt (3.2) – caused by anaerobic respiration and the production of lactic acid. After exercise the debt has to be repaid in order to break down the lactic acid.

P

pancreas (9.1, 10.4) – the organ that produces the hormone insulin.

parasite (7.3) – an organism that lives on or in another living organism, causing it harm.

partially permeable (1.4) – allowing certain molecules through but not others.

passive (1.3) – a passive process does not require an input of energy from respiration.

persistent (7.6) – a chemical that breaks down very slowly in the environment.

phenotype (10.7) – the expression of the gene e.g. tall, short, blue eyes etc.

phloem (5.1) – plant tissue that transports dissolved food around the plant.

phosphorus (5.3) – an essential mineral salt required by plants and animals.

photosynthesis (3.1, 5.1) – the process by which plants convert water and carbon dioxide into oxygen and glucose, using energy from the Sun.

phototropism (8.6) – a growth response in plants either towards or away from a light source.

plasma (6.3) – a pale-yellow liquid that forms the fluid part of the blood.

platelets (6.3) – small fragments of cells found in the blood and involved in blood clotting.

population (7.1) – a group of organisms of one species living together in a habitat.

predator (7.3) – an animal that hunts and kills other animals for food.

prey (7.3) – an animal that is hunted and killed for food by a predator.

productivity (7.6) – the yield of a crop or livestock that is made in a certain time.

progesterone (8.5) – a hormone produced by the ovary after the ovum has been released. It maintains the wall of the uterus during pregnancy.

protease (2.1) – an enzyme that digests protein.

protein (5.3) – a large molecule made from a combination of amino acids.

pulmonary (6.2) – relating to the lungs, e.g. pulmonary artery and vein.

pupil (8.1) – the hole in the iris through which light enters the eye.

pyramid of biomass (7.4) – a diagram that represents the total mass at each trophic level of a food chain.

Q

quadrat (7.1) – a square frame that is used to estimate the number of organisms in a particular area.

R

rate (5.2) – how quickly something happens.

recessive (10.7) – an allele that does not express itself in the phenotype unless two are present in the gene.

red blood cells (6.3) – blood cells that contain the red pigment haemoglobin, which carries oxygen from the lungs around the body.

reflex (8.3) – a rapid response to a stimulus brought about without conscious thought in order to protect an individual from damage.

reflex arc (8.3) – the pathway along which nerve impulses pass in a simple reflex action.

relay neurone (8.3) – a nerve cell in the CNS that passes impulses between two neurones.

respiration (3.1, 5.3) – the breaking down of glucose to release energy.

retina (8.1) – the layer of light sensitive cells lining the back of the eye.

rods (8.1) – light-sensitive cells in the retina that work in dim light but cannot detect colour.

root hairs (6.4) – cells found on the surface of a root that absorb water from the soil.

root nodules (7.5) – small growths from the roots of plants in the pea and bean family. They contain nitrogen-fixing bacteria.

S

salt (9.3) – a compound (sodium chloride ; NaCl) that is taken in with food and is excreted by the kidneys.

seedless fruit (8.7) fruit that develop without fertilisation of a flower and so do not contain seeds.

selective breeding (10.6) – a way of improving stock by selecting and breeding from those animals and plants that have the desired characteristics.

selective weedkiller (8.7) – artificial plant hormones that kill some plants but not others.

sensory neurone (8.3) – a nerve cell that carries impulses from a receptor to the CNS.

sex chromosomes (10.2) – the two chromosomes that determine sex. They are usually referred to as X and Y.

shivering (9.2) – rapid muscular contractions that generate heat and help to maintain the body's temperature.

skin (9.2) – tissue which surrounds the body and acts as a barrier against invading microbes.

specialisation (1.2) – the process by which cells have become adapted to perform only a certain function and so have become more efficient.

species (10.9) – a group of organisms that breeds and produces fertile offspring.

specific (2.1) – the characteristic of an enzyme in which it will only act on a certain reaction.

sperm (10.5) – a male sex cell.

spinal cord (8.3) – a large collection of neurones that runs up the vertebral column and joins with the brain.

spirometer (4.2) – a machine that is used to measure a person's breathing rate and depth.

starch (5.3) – a food storage substance produced by plants.

stomata (5.1) – small pores on the underside of a leaf that regulate the release of water, and allow release of oxygen and the absorption of carbon dioxide (singular = stoma).

survival of the fittest (10.9) – organisms that are best adapted to their environment tend to produce successful offspring, thus ensuing their survival.

sustainable (7.7) – the use of the Earth's resources at a rate at which they can be replaced.

sweating (9.2) – the release of liquid onto the skin to cool the body by latent heat of evaporation.

synapse (8.2) – a minute gap between two neurones.

system (1.2) – a collection of organs working together to perform related functions.

T

temperature (5.2, 6.5, 9.2) – a scale to compare the intensity of heat of different objects. Normal body temperature is 37°C.

testosterone (8.5) – a hormone, produced in the testes, that controls the male's secondary sex characteristics.

thorax (4.1) – the cavity in the body above the diaphragm that contains the lungs and heart.

tidal volume (4.2) – the volume of air exchanged in each breath.

tissue (1.2) – a collection of similar cells that work together to perform a particular function.

tissue fluid (6.1) – plasma minus the large blood protein molecules that has leaked out of blood vessels and bathes all the body's cells.

trachea (4.1) – a tube, strengthened by cartilage, which carries air between the mouth and the bronchi.

transpiration pull (6.5) – the force that pulls water up from the roots to the leaves.

tropic (8.6) – the growth response in plants to a directional stimulus.

turgid (1.4) – the condition in plant cells when the cytoplasm pushes against the cell wall.

U

urea (9.3) – a waste material produced from the breakdown of unwanted amino acids.

urine (9.3) – a solution of urea in water which is stored in the bladder prior to elimination.

V

vacuole (1.1) – part of a cell that contains fluid enclosed in a membrane.

valve (6.1, 6.2) – structure that prevents blood flowing backwards. They are found in the heart and in veins.

variation (10.3, 10.9) – differences that exist between organisms.

vascular bundle (6.4) – a collection of xylem and phloem vessels that transport food and water around a plant.

vegetarian (7.6) – a person who does not eat meat.

vein (6.1, 6.2) – a blood vessel that returns blood to the heart.

vena cava (6.2) – the large vein that returns blood from the body to the heart.

ventricle (6.2) – the lower two muscular chambers of the heart. The left ventricle pumps blood around the body; the right ventricle pumps blood to the lungs.

villi (2.3) – small finger-like projections in the small intestine that increase the surface area for absorption (singular = villus).

vital capacity (4.2) – the maximum amount of air that can be exchanged in one breath.

voluntary action (8.3) – a response to a stimulus which involves conscious thought.

W

water (9.3) – a molecule that is essential to all living organisms, enabling life processes to be carried out. It is reabsorbed in large amounts by kidney tubules.

water potential (1.4) – a measure of the tendency of a cell to lose or gain water by osmosis.

waxy cuticle (6.4) – waterproof layer found on the upper surface of most leaves.

white blood cells (6.3) – found in the blood and form part of the body's defence mechanism. They produce antibodies and engulf bacteria.

wilt (1.4) – the drooping of a plant when its cells become flaccid.

XYZ

X (10.2) – a sex chromosome. Females have two X chromosomes; males have only one.

xylem (5.1, 6.4) – conductive tissue found in plants that carries water up from the roots to the leaves.

Y (10.2) – a sex chromosome found in males.

Glossary (TB A1-A4)

Terms set in *bold italic* are higher-tier material.

A

Acetobacter (A3.2) – a bacteria that converts alcohol to vinegar.

active immunity (A4.4) – immunity that results from the body making its own antibodies.

adrenaline (A1.3) – a hormone released from the adrenal glands.

AIDS (A4.2) – acquired immune deficiency syndrome – the collection of diseases that results from destruction of the immune system following infection with HIV.

amino acid (A1.1) – basic building block of protein.

anaemia (Al.1) – a disease resulting from a lack of red blood cells.

antibiotic (A4.3) – a drug that is used internally to kill bacteria. Antibiotics do not kill viruses.

antibiotic resistance (A4.3) – bacteria that are not killed by a particular antibiotic are described as antibiotic resistant.

antibodies (A4.4) – chemicals produced by the body that help to destroy foreign invading organisms.

antiseptic (A4.3) – a chemical that is used externally to kill micro-organisms.

arid (A2.2) – a dry habitat with little available water.

artificial system (A2.1) – a system that classifies organisms on the basis of a single characteristic.

athlete's foot (A4.1) – a fungal infection of the foot.

autotrophic (A2.2) – the production of food from simple molecules, usually by photosynthesis.

B

bacteria (A4.1, A4.3) – a type of microscopic organism (singular = bacterium).

bases (A3.4) – the four chemicals designated A, T, C and G that code for the instructions of life on DNA.

binomial system (A2.1) – a method of naming organisms using two names, the first being the genus, the second the species.

C

canning (A3.1) – the process of preserving food by sealing it in a tin.

catalyst (A3.3) a chemical that increases the rate of reaction without being used up.

cerebellum (A1.5) – an area at the back of the brain responsible for the control of balance and co-ordinating movements.

cerebrum (A1.5) – the area at the top of the brain responsible for conscious thought.

chemical preservatives (A3.1) – chemicals that prevent the decay of food.

choice chamber (A2.3) – a device used to determine the preferred habitat of organisms.

cholesterol (A1.1) – a lipid-based molecule needed for the correct functioning of cell membranes. Excess cholesterol in the blood can block blood vessels, leading to coronary heart disease.

chymosin (A3.2, A3.5) – an enzyme that clots milk.

class (A2.1) – grouping of organisms in classification between phylum and order.

conditioned reflex (A1.5) – an automatic response that has been learnt and does not involve conscious thought.

contaminated (A3.1) – the presence of an unwanted substance or micro-organisms.

coronary arteries (A1.1) – the main blood vessels supplying the heart muscle with oxygenated blood.

curds (A3.2) – the semi-solid part of milk in the cheese-making process.

D

dental decay (A1.1) – the breakdown of the surface of the teeth, caused by acid produced by bacteria in the mouth.

dialysis machine (A1.4) – a device used by a person whose kidneys are not working to regulate the composition of the blood.

DNA (A3.4) – the molecule that codes for all the instructions needed to make an organism, and is also capable of replication.

dorsal root (A1.5) – the branch of a spinal nerve that carries sensory neurones into the spinal cord.

drying (A3.1) – removing water. Drying food prevents bacterial decay.

E

encoded (A3.5) – the sequence of bases that spells out the instructions in DNA.

end plate (A1.5) – a swelling at the end of a motor neurone that comes into close proximity to a muscle fibre. Transmitter substances are released from the end plate and stimulate the muscle fibre to contract.

enzyme (A3.3, A3.5) – organic catalyst that speeds up the rate of a reaction.

external fertilisation (A2.3) – the fusing of gametes outside the female's body.

extrinsic sugars (A1.1) – sugars in food that are not held in cells.

family (A2.1) – grouping of organisms in classification between order and genus.

fermentation vessel (A3.5) – a container used in industry in which micro-organisms carry out anaerobic processes.

food (A3.1) – the source of nutrients and fuel for the body.

freezing (A3.1) – use of sub-zero temperatures to preserve food.

fungi (A3.1, A4.1, A4.5) – a type of microscopic organism (singular = fungus).

gene (A3.4) – a section of DNA that codes for one specific instruction.

genus (A2.1) – grouping of organisms in classification between family and species (plural = genera).

gill bar (A2.3) – the part of a gill that carries blood vessels and supports the gill filaments.

gill filaments (A2.3) – the part of a gill responsible for gaseous exchange.

gill rakers (A2.3) – the part of a gill that filters water.

gills (A2.3) – paired structures in fish responsible for gaseous exchange.

graft (A4.5) – the process of adding tissue, usually from a different organism.

growth spurt (A1.2) – a phase of rapid growth that occurs during puberty.

H

heterotrophic (A2.2) – the intake of food as complex organic molecules.

HIV (A4.2) – human immunodeficiency virus – the virus that infects white blood cells and ultimately leads to AIDS.

hyphae (A4.1) – thread-like structures that form a fungus.

I

immune system (A4.2) – the body's defence against foreign organisms.

immunisation (A4.4) – the process of stimulating the body to produce antibodies to a specific antigen.

infectious (A4.1) – a disease that can be passed from one person to another.

internal fertilisation (A2.3) – the fusing of male and female gametes inside the female's body.

irradiation (A3.1) – the process of bombarding a substance with radiation.

kinesis (A2.3) – a behaviour pattern that involves more rapid movement in areas where conditions are unfavourable.

kidney tubules (A1.4) – structures in the kidney that filter the blood and modify the content of the filtrate.

kingdom (A2.1) – the first major grouping in classification. There are five kingdoms.

L

lactic acid (A3.2) – a chemical produced when *Lactobacillus* breaks down the milk sugar lactose. (It is also produced by anaerobic respiration in humans, and causes muscle fatigue.)

Lactobacillus (A3.2) – a bacteria that converts the milk sugar lactose into lactic acid.

Larva(e) (A2.3) – a stage in many insect life cycles between the egg and pupa (plural = larvae).

medulla (A1.3) – an area at the base of the brain responsible for many reflex control mechanisms.

meninges (A1.5) – protective membranes enclosing the brain and spinal cord.

metamorphosis (A2.3) – a complete change in body form.

moisture (A3.1) – water; required by all living organisms.

Mucor mieleli (A3.5) – a species of fungus.

mycelium (A4.1) – a network of hyphae that make up a fungus.

mycoprotein (A3.2) – a protein produced by a fungus.

myxomatosis (A4.4) – a disease of rabbits caused by the myxoma virus.

N

natural system (A2.1) – a system in which organisms are classified on the basis of the maximum number of common characteristics.

nephron (A1.4) – the functional unit of the kidney, consisting of a kidney tubule and blood vessels. There are millions of nephrons in each kidney.

O

optimum (A3.3) – the optimum conditions are those at which the rate of reaction is fastest.

order (A2.1) – grouping of organisms in classification between class and family.

P

parasite (A4.2) – an organism that lives on or in another living organism, causing it harm.

passive immunity (A4.4) – temporary immunity produced by preformed antibodies (which are injected, or are passed from mother to baby).

pasteurised (A3.2) – the process of destroying harmful bacteria in milk so that it is safe to drink.

pathogen (A4.4) – an organism that causes disease.

pectinase (A3.5) – an enzyme that breaks down pectin.

peristalsis (A1.1) – muscular contractions that move food along the digestive system.

phage (A4.3) – a virus that attacks bacteria.

phylum (A2.1) – groupings of organisms in classification between kingdom and class (plural = phyla).

potato blight (A4.5) – a fungal disease that affects potato plants.

protein (A3.4) – large molecule formed from a combination of amino acids.

R

rabies (A4.4) – a viral disease characterised by madness and convulsions.

recombinant (A3.4) – an alteration of the position or number of genes found in DNA.

reference nutrient intake (RNI) (A1.2) – the amount of a molecule in the diet that is needed per day by most people for normal health.

rickets (A1.1) – a disease characterised by weak bones, arising from lack of vitamin D.

RNA (A3.4) – a single-strand template of DNA.

root stock (A4.5) – the root to which a stem from another plant is grafted.

S

Salmonella (A3.1) – a species of bacteria that cause food poisoning.

saturated fatty acids (A1.1) – fatty acids that do not contain any double bonds.

scurvy (A1.1) – a disease characterised by bleeding gums, painful joints and slow healing of wounds, arising from lack of vitamin C.

skeletal muscles (A1.5) – muscles that bring about movement of the bones of the skeleton. These muscles are under conscious control.

smallpox (A4.4) – a disease characterised by fever and pustules, caused by a virus. It has been eradicated by a global immunisation programme.

species (A2.1) – a group of organisms that breeds and produces fertile offspring; the smallest grouping in classification.

specific (A3.3) – the characteristic of an enzyme in which it will only act on a certain reaction.

spore (A4.5) – a small reproductive body produced by fungi.

stomata (A4.5) – small pores on the underside of a leaf that regulate the release of water, and allow release of oxygen and the absorption of carbon dioxide (singular = stoma).

Streptococcus (A3.2) – a genus of bacteria.

stroke (A1.3) – a blockage or burst blood vessel in the brain, starving brain tissue of oxygen.

substrate (A3.3) – a substance acted upon by an enzyme.

syndrome (A4.2) – a collection of symptoms of a disease.

TU

taxonomy (A2.1) – the process of classifying organisms in groups.

tetanus (A4.1) – a disease caused by bacteria, characterised by muscle spasm and rigidity.

ultra-heat treatment (A3.1) – brief heating of milk to a high temperature to kill micro-organisms.

unsaturated fatty acids (A1.1) – fatty acids that contain one or more double bonds.

VWY

vegan (A1.2) – someone who does not eat or use animal products.

vegetarian (A1.2) – a person who does not eat meat.

ventral root (A1.5) – the branch of a spinal nerve that carries sensory neurones out of the spinal cord.

virulent (A4.4) – able to cause disease.

virus (A4.1, A4.2, A4.3) – a small packet of DNA or RNA that reproduces by invading cells.

warmth (A3.1) – heat; required by all living organisms.

water potential (A3.1) – a measure of the tendency of a cell to loss or gain water by osmosis.

weaned (A1.2) – the process of introducing solid food into a baby's diet.

whey (A3.2) – the liquid part of milk that is produced in the cheese-making process.

white blood cells (A4.2) – found in the blood and form part of the body's defence mechanism. They produce antibodies and engulf bacteria.

yeast (A3.2) – a fungus, species of which are used in the production of bread and alcoholic drinks.

The carbon cycle

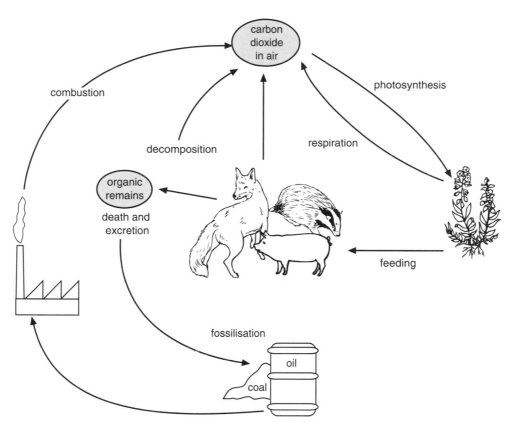

The nitrogen cycle

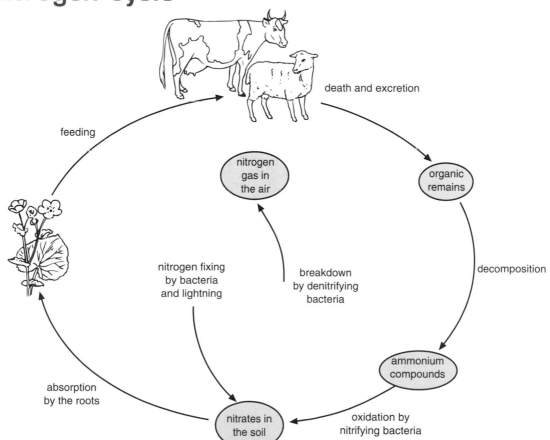

The respiratory system

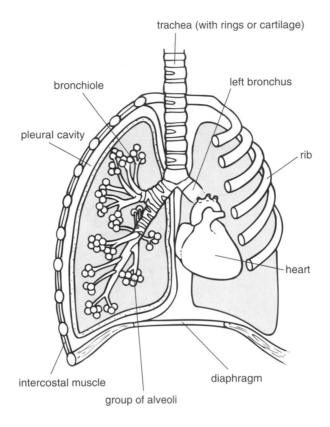

trachea (with rings or cartilage)

bronchiole

left bronchus

pleural cavity

rib

heart

intercostal muscle

group of alveoli

diaphragm

Cross-section of a leaf

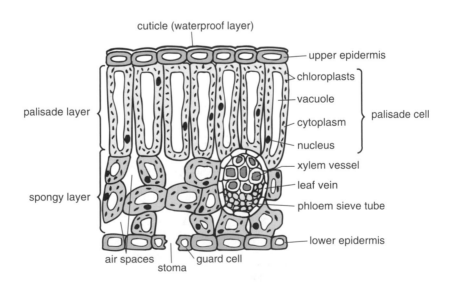

cuticle (waterproof layer)

upper epidermis

chloroplasts

vacuole

palisade cell

cytoplasm

palisade layer

nucleus

xylem vessel

leaf vein

spongy layer

phloem sieve tube

lower epidermis

air spaces

stoma

guard cell

Index